Starting with a Smallholding

David Hills

Broad Leys Publishing Ltd

Starting with a Smallholding

First published by Broad Leys Publishing Ltd: 2004

Copyright © 2004. David Hills

Editor: Katie Thear

A catalogue record for this book is available from the British Library.

ISBN: 0906137 37 3

Cover photographs: Katie Thear

Unless indicated otherwise, photographs inside the book were taken by Katie Thear

For details of other publications please see page 96.

Broad Leys Publishing Ltd
1 Tenterfields,
Newport, Saffron Walden,
Essex CB11 3UW, UK.
Tel/Fax: 01799 541065
E-mail: kdthear@btinternet.com
Website: www.kdthear.btinternet.co.uk

Contents

Foreword

Starting with a Smallholding provides a blueprint for anyone about to buy a smallholding, or who wishes to make productive use of a little land. This may be anything from a large garden and small orchard to several acres, but whatever the scale, the following factors need to be taken into consideration: Space, Time, Energy and Costs. (Interest is taken as read!)

The book does not claim to be comprehensive, or to provide a wealth of practical detail. Instead, it concentrates on the salient points of each smallholding activity, whilst pointing the reader in the right direction for further information. At the end of each enterprise, for example, there is a summary of the space, time, energy and costs involved. The summaries include the following symbols:

❑	=	Space
🕐	=	Time
✋	=	Energy
£	=	Costs

To show the relative amount in each case, one, two or three of each symbol are used. For example:

❑❑❑🕐🕐✋✋£

This would be interpreted as follows:

> A few acres of land are required.
> A fair amount of time and energy are needed.
> The costs are relatively low.

Introduction

In conversations I and others have lately discussed the practice of farming.
You will find in them the practical information that you need.
(On Farming. Varro. 46BC)

This book is intended to provide guidelines for anyone planning to start or take on an existing smallholding. It first began as a small booklet entitled *The Smallholding Plan* which proved so popular that it had to be reprinted several times. Now, it has been expanded into a book and concentrates on choosing and setting up a smallholding, taking into account not only the different characteristics of smallholdings but also the circumstances of the intending smallholder. It provides basic information on the various activities associated with keeping livestock and poultry, and then details where further information and help may be obtained in each case.

Every aspect of smallholding life consumes time, energy and money in differing amounts. A young family needing to bring in an income may be short of time and money but have plenty of energy. A recently retired couple may have limited energy available but some reserves of time and money. These factors determine the type of holding that is appropriate. Accordingly, and as referred to opposite, some sections conclude with a summary of the time, energy and costs involved, together with an appreciation of the space required and details of where further information may be obtained.

Buying property with land as a smallholding is more complicated than simply choosing a home. Young people with lots of ideas and energy believe sometimes that they can achieve anything, but a poor choice can wear down anyone over time. As a smallholder for many years, I well recall the mistakes we made in the first months, taking on more and more livestock too quickly and paying the price when we were unprepared for soaring feed bills, escaping animals and trying to cope when suffering from the 'flu!

It pays to think through any major move in a realistic way, facing up to the worst possible scenarios before they happen. Define your aims and aspirations and jot them down. Look at each potential smallholding or activity coolly and see whether it really meets your needs. A large kitchen garden and poultry and livestock to feed and milk daily, can be deeply satisfying but it can also be a tie and may become a burden.

For the inexperienced, starting with a smallholding requires careful planning beforehand, then practical preparation before undertaking each new enterprise. In other words, take one step at a time and don't put the cart before the horse.

(David Hills, 2004)

5

Preparations

Politics is perhaps the only profession for which no preparation is thought necessary. (Y. Torajiro. 1882)

Wherever you choose to live, and whatever the final activities on your smallholding, it is essential to clarify your ideas on what you want to do and how you will be able to make it pay.

Where does the money come from?

Many people have found that selling an expensive urban property has enabled them to buy a cheaper property in the countryside. If this is the case, all well and good, but in recent years the relative difference between town and country properties has decreased.

A smallholding is unlikely to pay for itself, unless a specialised activity to supply a niche market is undertaken. In most cases, a separate income is required. What this will be obviously depends on the individual.

If you need to borrow money from the bank, finance or mortgage company, the lender will want reassurance that you will be in a position to keep up with the payments. Whether you need to borrow or not, it is useful to make a business plan and work out your cashflow for the first two years. This will sound daunting if you have not done it before, but it is not really difficult. Your bank has free literature on the subject. The great benefit is the demand it makes to clarify your ideas, to cost them and to be realistic.

Where do the skills come from?

Smallholding life is all about practical tasks, many of which will be unfamiliar at the beginning. Equip yourself for this particular journey by learning practical skills before you buy. The following will pay dividends:

- Building construction and maintenance
- Basic plumbing and electrics.
- Machinery and vehicle maintenance and repairs.
- Poultry and livestock husbandry.
- Lambing skills
- Pasture maintenance

There are dozens of other skills that can be learned like beekeeping, woodland and textile crafts, cheesemaking, growing organic crops and so on, according to how you plan to use your smallholding. Gaining these skills and experience beforehand will give you invaluable knowledge and confidence later, and will save you making costly mistakes.

Is a Smallholding for You?

Pros

There are estate agents who specialise in selling smallholdings.

It is possible to combine a smallholding activity with a non-land based business that operates from home.

Working from home can be very satisfying.

A country lifestyle can be healthy and rewarding for adults and children.

It is possible to produce good quality, fresh food that is free of additives.

There are many courses of practical instruction available covering all aspects of smallholding life, organic growing and animal husbandry.

There are often local groups where help and information are available.

DEFRA (Department of Food & Rural Affairs) provides information and guidelines on small farming enterprises.

Local farmers' markets provide sales outlets for fresh produce.

It is possible to start small and test the market before going into full production.

For many people it's the lifestyle they've always wanted.

Cons

Smallholdings that are reasonably priced are increasingly hard to find.

It may be hard to combine earning a living from another source with the demands of a smallholding.

It can be difficult to make money from smallholding activities unless they are specialised and catering for specific markets.

Combining production and the selling of produce may be difficult because there is not enough time or help available.

It may be difficult to find a reasonably priced smallholding which is also close to good schools and other facilities.

Everyone in the family needs to be commited to the lifestyle.

Hard, physical work is involved.

The hours are often long.

A thorough knowledge of animal husbandry and welfare is needed.

Holidays may be difficult to organise.

Some may find it difficult to adapt to the realities of smallholding life, eg, the slaughter of animals and poultry raised for meat.

Regulations in relation to the keeping of livestock and the selling of produce must be followed.

Sound fencing is essential to keep animals out of where they shouldn't be! It needs to be in place before the animals are introduced to the site,

A small tractor is often the workhorse of the smallholding, but ideally should have a safety roll bar. There are courses available on tractor and machinery maintenance.

Courses

Skills that are applicable in town and country can be undertaken at evening courses. Short courses that teach country skills are more specialised and are available at agricultural colleges, farms, smallholdings and local farm training groups, as well as other country organisations. Country courses are usually advertised in smallholding magazines, particularly around July/August for those beginning in the autumn. They may be residential for a week or two, or just last a weekend. It is a good idea to undertake as many courses as you can *before* taking on the smallholding, for there will be less time available after you have taken the plunge. One bonus of courses is the knowledge and confidence that comes from meeting others.

Where does further help and information come from?

Once installed, the smallholder will need practical help with running the smallholding, and will look to more comprehensive books. The best and most up to date is *The Smallholder's Manual* by Katie Thear, published by Crowood Press, which is really excellent. Other suggestions are listed at the end of individual chapters or in the *Reference* section.

Information can also be gained by reading magazines such as *Country Smallholding* and *The Smallholder*. Then, there are organisations such as the *Department of the Environment, Food and Rural Affairs (DEFRA)*, as well as local smallholding organisations. The library usually has a list of local organisations. They are also usually listed in smallholding magazines such as those referred to above. For more information see the *Reference section*.

Animal welfare codes

All livestock and poultry must be kept according to the welfare codes that are specified for them. Free copies are available from *DEFRA*. There are also regulations that apply in some cases. These are referred to later.

Is a smallholding for you?

The table on the previous page may be useful for those who are undecided about whether a smallholding is a practical reality. However, it is important to define your own aims and aspirations, for every situation is different. It is also vital to consult *all* the family members, otherwise it may be a case of one person rushing off in a direction that others may be reluctant to follow.

Make a list of your plans and requirements, then put it away. About a week later read through what you have written. After a short space of time such as this, it is surprising how it is possible to be much more objective. It is almost like reading what someone else has written. Does it still make sense? If it does, good luck!

What is a Smallholding?

One may compare small things with great. (Virgil. 10BC)

During the first half of the twentieth century there were thousands of smallholders throughout Britain, making a living from growing fruit and vegetables, keeping chickens, and sometimes rabbits and a couple of pigs. Changing economic conditions, aided by deliberate government policy, led to a massive decline in the numbers of smallholdings and small mixed family farms during the 1940s and 1950s. By the 1970s, making a full time living from a smallholding was practically impossible, and today this is also true for the small farm. Those that have survived have specialised or found other supplementary sources of income.

People today who regard themselves as smallholders are a diverse group, consisting of traditional small farmers and newcomers who have moved into country houses with land to practise a degree of self sufficiency and small scale farming as a desirable lifestyle. The idea that one can be fully self sufficient from an acre or two is nonsense. The idea of making a viable living is also unrealistic unless, as referred to earlier, it is specialised to cater for a niche market. What is possible is that a smallholding can produce good wholesome food for the family. It can also be used as a base for a home business which may or may not have a connection with the land.

Generally speaking, there needs to be further income from other sources to make ends meet. There is no defining amount of land or activity that makes a smallholding. Even those with just a garden can make use of it.

A garden
A small or medium sized garden can be used to grow some fruits and vegetables, keep a few chickens, ducks, quails and rabbits, and if conditions are right, a couple of hives of bees.

It becomes possible to increase the scale of food raising activities with a larger garden or accompanying allotment. It may also be possible to earn a small income from selling cut flowers, eggs, organic produce and honey. This increased activity will begin to eat into resources of time and energy

A one acre smallholding
Extra space provides the opportunity to add a couple of goats and pigs to the enterprise, to provide milk and home reared meat, but it will be necessary to buy in all their fodder such as hay, as well as providing buildings and veterinary care. The costs and time involved will be greater.

A five acre smallholding

This should be sufficient to undertake any activity commensurate with a part time smallholding, including keeping some sheep or a house cow. More land still will increase both choice and flexibility in the type and scale of any enterprise, but will make more demands on time, energy and money.

A registered smallholding

If you keep animals (not poultry) on your smallholding, you must register as a keeper with *DEFRA*. Contact your nearest *Regional Office* and ask for the *Farm Records* section. You will be given a *CPH (County, Parish, Holding) number*. In 2005 this process will be centralised to one office in Newcastle.

Movements of farm animals away from the smallholding are subject to controls and in many cases a licence or other documentation is required. Information on this can be obtained from your local *Trading Standards* department which is responsible for *Animal Health* and *Agricultural Standards*.

If you plan to run a small farm as a profitable business, there is help available from the *Farm Business Advice Service*. This has been developed between *DEFRA* and the *Small Business Service (SBS)* and is available locally through *Business Links*. Essentially, up to three days of professional advice is provided free of charge resulting in an action plan. This service is open to all farmers in England who have a *CPH* number and who spend at least 75% or their time at the core farm business. Information can be obtained from the *SBS* on 0845 600 9006

An organic smallholding

If you wish to produce organic products from the smallholding, there is free advice available from the Organic Conversion Information Service (OCIS) through a number of independent helplines. This covers organic standards, certification, organic farming schemes, conversion details, technical advice, and information on markets. Helplines are:

England Tel: 0117 922 7707
Wales Tel: 01970 622 100
Scotland Tel: 01224 711 072
N. Ireland Livestock Tel: 028 9442 6752/6614, Crops Tel: 028 9442 6765

To sell produce described as organic, it is necessary to be registered with a recognised certification body such as the *Soil Association* or the *Organic Farmers & Growers*. (See References). However, the cost of organic registration may not be justified on a very small scale. In this case it may be better to produce food to the best standard that you can and sell it directly at the farm gate or at the local market or farmer's market.

Choosing the Smallholding

You pays your money and you takes your choice. (Punch. 1846)

There is a real danger in buying 'a dream place in the country', which is both impractical and unsuitable. Practical considerations are easily downgraded in favour of a dream. Beware! Such a purchase will soon reveal the disadvantages of the holding and can result in many difficulties. So powerful is a dream, that it is better to view smallholdings in poor weather, ideally with rain, mud and in cold conditions.

Before focusing on particular properties, decide which area would be most suitable for your circumstances. This is often determined first by cost, then by local conditions of climate and surrounding facilities.For most people the three main considerations are likely to be:

• Price of the property and its size and condition.
• Condition of the attached land, fencing and outbuildings
• Geographical location and local facilities

The price of anything is a reflection of supply and demand. Houses with land in attractive areas within easy reach of cities are invariably expensive and unsuitable for the prospective smallholder. Many smallholders, during the last 25 years, have moved to Wales and the south-west of England where the climate is mild and property affordable. Some have moved further afield to Ireland, France and Spain.

Climate in the United Kingdom, with the exception of the Scottish Highlands, is often determined more by height and exposure to winds than geographical position. There are however some general considerations. The west has more rain and milder winters than the east, and the growing season becomes shorter as you move north. The following detailed list may be useful in checking one property against another to see how they score.

House
The house is the prime consideration. It needs to be right before anything else is considered.

• Is the house suitable for you and your family?
• Is there sufficient space for your needs, or will it need extending?
• What repairs and renovations are needed?
• What are the costs and time scale needed to adapt the house to your needs?
• What are the likely annual running costs? - council tax, heating etc.
• Are there restrictions on altering the house? - listed building, agricultural dwelling etc.

Services

Reliable services of the right quality are essential. Make sure they are right before you buy.

• Are the available services satisfactory?
• Is there mains water or is the supply from a private source?
• Does the private source supply enough water all year at required quality?
• Is there mains sewage or a septic tank?
• Will the septic tank need renewing, and if so at what cost?
• Is there a mains gas supply?
• Is there mains electricity? If not, is there a generator?
• What is the capacity, condition and cost of running the generator, how reliable is it, and when will it need replacing?
• What are the possibilities, costs and time scale for switching from local sources to mains supplies?

Access and situation

There's no substitute for doing really thorough homework before deciding to go ahead. The house and land may be ideal but it is not the whole story.

• Is there easy access to a main road? Is it a shared access?
• Does the access road need repair or renovation? If so at what cost?
• Is the entrance via a mud track and will you need a 4x4 vehicle?
• Are there existing local problems of noise, pollution, heavy traffic, difficult neighbours or other hazards?
• Are there future problems from planned new roads, housing or industry?

Garden

A garden can be developed, but heavy clay or poor soil and persistent weeds like ground elder will be a constant burden.

• Is the existing garden suitable for your needs?
• What is the size and state of the garden?
• What are the prevalent weeds? Is there ground elder?
• Is the garden organic or have chemicals been used regularly?
• What is the composition and pH of the soil?
• What fruit trees and bushes are there? What is their condition?
• Is there an orchard? What does it consist of and what is its condition?

Land

Every smallholder needs good level land and well built outbuildings.

• Is the land suitable for your needs?
• Is the land level or sloping? Is it north or south facing?

- How high is the property?
- What are the climatic conditions throughout the year?
- Is the land sheltered or exposed? Are there frost pockets?
- Are the fields of a convenient size and shape?
- What is the type and condition of the soil? Have chemicals been applied?
- Is there weed infestation - docks, nettles, ragwort, bracken, etc?
- What is the state of the drainage? Are there rushes in the pasture?
- What trees are on the site?
- What are the condition of the hedges and ditches?
- What are the condition of the fences and gates?
- Is there rubbish on the site? Will the seller remove it before you buy?
- What outbuildings are there? What is their construction and condition?
- Is there evidence of vermin?
- Is there machinery included in the sale? Does it work, and what is it worth?
- Are there footpaths or rights of way across the land?
- Are there shooting, fishing or other rights?

Local facilities

Again, even the best smallholding in a perfect setting may not be suitable if business, medical, scholastic and social needs are difficult to access.

- Do the local facilities meet all your needs?
- What is the potential for farm gate or local produce sales?
- Is the property in a tourist area? Is there potential for bed and breakfast?
- What are the local employment prospects?
- How far are the nearest village or town shopping facilities?
- How far away are schools? Is there transport available? Are your children eligible for the schools of your choice?
- Is there sufficient public transport?
- How far away is the nearest doctor, dentist or hospital?
- Are there suitable social venues nearby? - church, pub, youth club, etc.
- How far away are cinemas, theatres, restaurants, concert halls etc?
- Finally, have you examined the house, land and surroundings on a cold, wet, winter's day?

Running a business from a smallholding

If you intend running a business from the site, it may be necessary to apply for 'change of use' planning permission. Where new buildings are to be erected, planning and building permission will also be needed. Contact the local authority for information. In addition to all the mains services, a computer with internet access is vital these days. Aim to have a Broadband net access for speed, convenience and cost saving.

Buying Livestock and Poultry

Don't buy a pig in a poke!

Before purchasing any poultry or livestock, learn about the animals you intend to buy. Read about them, join a local smallholding group or breed club where appropriate. Go on courses, attend shows and talk to breeders, before selecting the breed(s) you want. Rare and minority breed shows are particularly useful for contacting breeders and seeing their stock.

Have everything ready!

Prepare beforehand so that all the necessary conditions are ready for the newcomers. This includes the housing, feeders and drinkers, together with the feedstuffs that they will need. The latter will need to be stored in rodent-free containers. There should be adequate fencing to confine the animals. This may involve checking and strengthening hedges and fences, or installing electric netting. The pasture should also be in good heart and free of toxic plants such as ragwort.

Other preparations include having facilities for keeping records. These include movement licences and veterinary records. The *Animal Health* department of the local *Trading Standards* office will provide details, as well as information on tagging and identification of animals.

When animals are bought, they will obviously need to be transported to the smallholding. The seller may do this, otherwise the buyer will need to arrange it. A vehicle or trailer that provides safe conditions that meet the requirements of the *Welfare of Animals (Transport) Order* will be needed

What to look for

Try to buy birds or animals that you can look at first. Healthy animals have bright eyes with a sheen to their coats or feathers and are responsive in a positive way. See that they walk without limping and that there are no obvious defects. If they are claimed to be good representatives of their breed, make sure that you know what the breed looks like and, if possible, take an experienced person with you. Avoid buying animals in the market. Where appropriate, have two or more of the same type. An animal without one of its own kind will be discontented.

If buying stock without viewing beforehand, ensure that they come from a respected source and have had the necessary injections so that you are not importing disease. All newly introduced stock should be kept in quarantine, away from other animals and poultry for about ten days. This allows sufficient time for any problems to become apparent, and helps to prevent the passing on of infections to existing stock.

Chickens

Chickens can be bought as hybrids which are specialised for meat or egg laying, or as pure breeds for interest and breeding. Whatever you buy, make sure that the birds have been inoculated against Marek's and Newcastle diseases and have come from a salmonella enteriditus free flock.

• **Fertile eggs**: These are not advisable for the beginner as many things can go wrong and they are best handled by someone experienced.

• **Day olds**: These are cheap to buy but need protected, heated conditions, and rearing for four months before they will lay.

• **Growers**: At about 6 weeks old, these are dearer than day olds, are off heat, and will need grower's rations for the next 12-14 weeks.

• **Point of Lay** (POL): This is the best option for a new smallholder although POLs are the most expensive at around 18 weeks old. All the rearing has been done and they will have a little time to settle into their new house before starting to lay. Check that they are perch trained, request that they are not beak trimmed, and check what they have been fed.

• **Battery birds**: Commercial batteries cast out their hybrid layers at one year old and they can be bought cheaply. They will look terrible with few feathers and will be reluctant to go outside at first. They will gradually recover and should be reasonably productive birds. Bear in mind, though, that you could be importing diseases and you will not be allowed to sell their eggs as organic ones.

• **Pure breeds**: Buy pure breeds either locally or through one of the breed directories or advertisements in poultry or smallholding magazines. If planning a breeding programme, obtain the male from a different source.

Sheep

Sheep are best purchased from specialist breeders. Choose pure pedigree animals, although they cost more. If possible, visit the farm and look at the flock and pedigree details. They will be the foundation of your future flock and if you come to sell lambs in later years they will fetch a better price than non-pedigree sheep.

Choose sheep suited to your area, avoiding overlarge breeds. Why do you want to keep sheep? If it is primarily for meat or perhaps coloured wool this will also be a factor in the selection. Good sheep should stand square with straight legs and strong wide shoulders. See that the udder has no lumps, and check the mouth to see that the incisors and the upper pad meet correctly and that there are no broken teeth. Breeders' directories in smallholding magazines and the magazine of the *Rare Breeds Survival Trust (RBST)* are good sources of contacts.

Pigs

If you are beginning with just a couple of weaners, it is sensible to buy them from a local farmer. You can, at the same time, get some useful advice from him about feeding and when to slaughter.

If you want pigs to breed from, then choose pedigree animals from a recognised breeder. A traditional breed would be a good choice as they are well suited to smallholdings. Good pigs have a straight back with good meaty hams and a clear shiny coat. They should also have a curly tail and clean ears, be a good size for their age and move easily without limping. Avoid snuffling pigs with runny eyes, or swellings around the jawline.

Goats

Join the local goat club, and having selected your breed(s), buy from a respected local breeder. You can check on the pedigree and registration on the spot. Goatkeepers are always helpful and your local contacts will be a valuable source of advice in the first year.

When buying kids, look at the mother. A good milking goat has a long fine neck, narrow shoulders, a deep and wide chest. She will be large with good length and depth in the body. The udder will be spherical in shape with even teats and no lumps, and she will walk easily without limping.

Cows

To stay productive a milking cow will have to calve every year. Ensure that you are fully prepared for this before you buy. For the smallholder, a Jersey or Dexter cow may be appropriate as both their size and milk production are in the right scale. Having decided on a breed, ask local farmers, neighbours and the vet for possible sources. Also contact the particular breed society about their local members.

Sometimes a farmer will sell a 5-6 year old cow which is halfway through her milking life. Be careful about farm sales and retirement sales as the price can be high. Always avoid buying from a market.

When viewing a cow look for a pliable and well shaped, soft udder with even teats and no lumps. Check that she has a good coat with bright eyes and doesn't limp. Ask to see her registration details and her milking records before agreeing to buy. She should also come with a cattle 'passport' for this is required for all cows, whether they are dairy or beef cattle.

17

Getting Started

What we call the beginning is often the end,
And to make an end is to make a beginning. (T S Elliot)

Once the property is bought, the temptation is to try and tackle every thing at once. This doesn't work because with a new enterprise, changes need to be undertaken carefully, step by step, to avoid making unnecessary errors and secondly, some things have to be done in order. For example, animals cannot be put into a field where they could wander onto the road. Fences need to be checked and repaired beforehand.

One of the attractions of smallholding life is the varied nature of the different enterprises that can be undertaken, but every task consumes time, energy and money. This book will consider these aspects, as well as space requirements, in the forthcoming chapters.

Priorities

The first priority will not produce any food nor bring in any income, but it is the base from which everything else flows - the house. If the house needs repairs and renovation to make it habitable and acceptable as a working home for all the family, then it needs to be tackled first. If necessary, put the rest of the holding onto a care and maintenance basis while the house is renovated. If planning has been done beforehand, the necessary resources will be available. Failure to put the house first can result in problems which may be difficult to put right when there are other commitments later on. Of course, it may not be practical to tackle everything that needs doing in the house at the outset, but a plan can be made and the essentials dealt with on a priority basis.

Once you are settled in and the house is on its way, you can look at your original plans from the present standpoint and begin to put them into action. Smallholding life can be demanding, so proceed step by step, making sure that you are comfortable with each stage before moving on to the next.

House

If the house is old and in need of renovation, your survey report will provide an overall picture of its condition and give some pointers to what needs to be done. If you have taken out a mortgage on the property, the lender may require certain work to be undertaken within a fixed period, and will come round to check that it has been done. You can call in the professionals - builder, electrician, plumber, etc, for their estimates of how much work is needed, how long it will take and what it will cost. Make sure that you

It is essential to have good fencing for the grass is always greener on the other side

obtain more than one quote for each job. Armed with this information you can schedule the work and decide what you can undertake yourself, and what needs to be done by others. You can certainly save money by doing the work if you have the time, confidence and expertise. If you are a practical person, it is surprising how much renovation work can be undertaken successfully, even if you haven't done it before. In a way, this is the first test for the new smallholder, as there will be innumerable tasks ahead such as repairing barns and sheds, livestock housing, fences, gates, and so on.

Land and garden

Nothing stands still! The grass in the fields, the hedges, and the weeds everywhere will grow vigorously from spring to autumn. This has to be managed otherwise everything will deteriorate, requiring extra effort to bring it back under control. A clear appreciation of what needs to be done, and when, is needed at the outset. A priority is to ensure that the boundaries - hedges, fences and ditches are adequate and secure.

With a clear plan established for the house, the garden can be tackled. A good long term plan for the garden is a good idea and you can begin straight away deciding where vegetables and fruit bushes are going to be sited. Whatever the time of year, ground can be cleared and planting can begin.

These pigs have done an excellent job of ploughing the soil, getting rid of roots and making the area ready for cultivation. They are also doing what they like best!

Compost heaps are essential to build up and maintain soil fertility. Meanwhile, this one is also being used to grow courgettes.

Growing

With mine own hand I wrought to make it grow.
(Rubaiyat of Omar Khayyam, 1859)

If one is lucky, a smallholding may already have a kitchen garden and it could just be a matter of catching up with bed reclamation, weeding and planting. Nine times out of ten, however, it is a case of having to start from scratch with an area of ground that is either grass covered or weed infested.

Preparing the ground

There is no point in killing yourself trying to dig this over. It is much better to mark out the area, cover it with thick black plastic or old carpets, weight them down and leave for a season. Plant growth will be killed off in this way and the earthworm population will boom while doing an excellent job of aerating and fertilising the soil underneath the cover.

It may be that you can't wait that long, so the best option in that case is to buy or hire an agricultural flame gun to clear the vegetation. The area can then be dug, rotovated or ploughed depending on the size, but beware, the underlying roots will still be there and will need to be cleared away.

Pigs are some of the best natural ploughers and can be used to prepare the ground for you. Provide a moveable house for them and fence off the area, a section at a time, so that they can get to work. They will not only turn the soil but will also crunch their way through most of the roots, while their droppings add fertility to the soil.

Chickens will also clear an area of ground in a similar way, although their activities tend to concentrate on the top layer of the soil only. Even so, their scratching and dustbathing soon loosen the vegetation and turn the soil over.

Once the ground is relatively clear, a traditional practice is to plant some seed potatoes as a clearing crop. As they grow the potatoes break up the soil, leaving it in a more friable condition for the next crop.

Planning the kitchen garden

Growing crops is time consuming and hard work. On a home scale the saving over bought produce is comparatively small, although over the whole season some crops do make a profit, so why do it? The answer, is that producing one's own food is rewarding because the quality and freshness is often superior to bought produce. Growing your own also provides a range of choices. Within the limits of the soil and climatic conditions, it is possible to select the crops and varieties to grow to suit the needs of your family. Surpluses can be stored or frozen for future consumption and those unsuitable for storage can be fed to livestock. Pigs for example are partial to fresh apples and cooked potatoes.

When starting a new garden or taking on an established one, check that it is in the best place, protected from winds and with the maximum exposure to sun. Work out the area needed for the planned garden and then add a bit. It is always good to have some ground in hand as plans will change during the first few years. Look at the type and depth of productive soil. Will it suit your needs or does it need a great deal of additional organic matter to provide the humus that the plants need to thrive? It is always a good idea to check the pH value of the soil with a soil testing kit so that the relative acidity or alkalinity can be established. If it is too acidic, the addition of lime is vital, just as it is for growing brassicas. If too alkaline, the soil can be balanced by the addition of rotted manure and compost. It may be necessary to buy in manure or organic fertiliser until you are in a position to supply your own from the smallholding. Spent mushroom compost and horse manure are available in most areas. Start a series of compost heaps as soon as possible, but don't put perennial weeds in them.

If growing mainly to provide for family needs, choose the crops and varieties accordingly. Make sure you get all the available seed catalogues! Raise crops that provide a good yield in relation to the ground used and which cannot be bought cheaply elsewhere.

One advantage of growing one's own is that flavoursome varieties can be chosen. (For commercial reasons, these rarely appear in supermarkets). Fruits and vegetables can be picked at their peak and eaten straight away. One of my abiding happy memories as a child is helping my grandmother collect potatoes and pick peas from the garden. They tasted wonderful.

Grow those crops that will do well in your soil and utilise the disease resistant varieties. Some crops may not be worth growing at all because the soil is not suitable, they take up too much space, or they need too much work. One example is maincrop potatoes. I haven't grown them for years, as I can buy them organically grown by the sack at a nearby farm. Early varieties are different and I always grow them for delicious new potatoes.

Raised beds
It might be a good idea to convert part of the growing area to raised beds. A raised bed is usually about 2.5m x 1.25m (8ft long x 4ft wide), the width being sufficient for hand weeding and cropping without needing to step onto the bed. To make a raised bed, first mark out the area, then dig over the soil about 30cms (1ft) deep and mix in some well rotted manure. Next put

in the frame around the bed, something like a 25cm x 2.5cm (10in x 1in) board fixed firmly at the corners. Fill to the brim with more topsoil and manure or compost. Leave straight paths between the raised beds, sufficient for a mower or wheelbarrow. If you are using a raised bed system because you find digging difficult, the original digging over could be done with a cultivator.

Raised beds have many advantages, apart from the fact that the soil is not compacted by being walked on. Plants can be grown more closely together because there is a deeper expanse of topsoil, and it is easy to cover them with horticultural fleece or cloches for early production. Pests such as onion and carrot fly that tend to fly low can also be excluded by having raised walls around the bed. For example, an extra 30cm (12in) of plastic walling above the bed boarding is effective.

Vegetables and herbs

Half hardy plants such as tomatoes can be started under cover and transferred into the garden later when the soil has warmed up. Seeds planted straight into the soil need a fine tilth with large lumps broken down with a rake. Avoid pest build up by not planting the same crop in one place year after year. The principle of crop rotation is well known and there are many different ways of doing it. The two main points are that roots should not follow potatoes as they need different soil conditions. Similarly, peas and beans like well limed soil but potatoes do not, so avoid following legumes with potatoes. The following four year crop rotation is widely used and it has always been effective for me:

1:	**Potatoes**	**Roots**	**Brassicas**	**Legumes**
	Manure.	No manure.	Manure at digging.	Manure at digging
	No lime.	Lime in spring.	Lime at planting.	Lime at planting.
2:	Legumes	Potatoes	Roots	Brassicas
3:	Brassicas	Legumes	Potatoes	Roots
4:	Roots	Brassicas	Legumes	Potatoes - and so on..

Different herbs need differing growing conditions and require varied space requirements. As some need a great deal of space, it may be best to have a small herb bed near to the house for commonly used culinary herbs, and another bed in the kitchen garden for the larger ones.

When it comes to keeping annual weeds at bay, a good hoe is the organic gardener's best tool. If possible, use a seep hose or other form of irrigation which takes water straight to the roots and avoids waste. Pick crops regularly to maximise production.

There are specialist suppliers who supply organic alternatives to using chemical sprays. (See *Reference Section*). In fact, it pays to avoid the chemical treadmill altogether because pests build up resistance and their residues can be harmful to wildlife and consumers.

A visit to the HDRA organic gardens at Ryton is highly recommended for anyone who is about to start an organic garden. Visitors are guaranteed to come away with good practical ideas, information and enthusiasm.

Soft fruit

Soft fruit bushes are a good example of growing what you like and making good use of the available ground. Raspberries are a vertical crop taking up very little ground area, and, provided you have a selection of different varieties, can fruit through the summer into autumn. Provide them with strong poles for support. Pruning is simply a matter of cutting out the fruited canes at the end of the season and then tying in the new, green canes which will fruit next year. Mulch them with compost or rotted manure.

Strawberries take up a lot of space and are cheap to buy at the market or pick-your-own places in midsummer, but many people do like to grow them because they are so delicious. If you decide to do so, choose good-flavoured varieties otherwise they are a waste of time. Again, ensure that you have all the appropriate catalogues so that you know what the options are. (See *Reference Section*).

Blackcurrants are easy to grow, and if you buy the more modern varieties, you are less likely to be bothered with diseases such as 'big bud' or leaf reversion. Rhubarb seems to grow in any shady patch and forcing it, by covering it to exclude the light in early spring, provides fruit when little else is available from the kitchen garden. Gooseberries are best planted as two-year old plants. After fruiting, pruning is a matter of cutting over-long and crossing branches, and then keeping the centre of the bush open.

Fruit growing smallholdings where there are a lot of hungry birds are vulnerable. If this is a problem then protecting the soft fruit with a fruit cage is the answer and it will pay for itself over the years. It can be bought or made at home with poles and plastic netting. Open the top for pollinating insects early in the season, and in winter to avoid snow damage.

Top fruit

Fruit trees don't need to be near to the house as they only need occasional attention. They can be grown in an orchard or, if space is limited, they can be trained to grow flat alongside a wall or fence. Favourites are cooking and eating apples, pears and the inimitable and delicious Victoria plum which is self-pollinating so you only need one. Choose and buy trees during the

Part of the organic kitchen garden at Ryton, showing raised beds being used to grow vegetables.

winter months when the plants are dormant. Top fruit can be bought as standard or half standard trees, bush, cordon, fan trained or espalier. Be clear about the eventual size of each tree and plant accordingly. The different rootstocks on which they are grown will determine the height, and the shorter ones are obviously easier to harvest. Remember also that although some fruit trees are self-pollinating, others need to be pollinated by different trees, so you will need to choose those that are compatible. Good suppliers will provide the necessary information and advice. Trees can be bought at local garden centres or from specialised nurseries that advertise in gardening and smallholding magazines.

It is likely that there will be existing fruit trees on a smallholding and probably past their best, having grown too large and fruiting intermittently. (Some trees, such as the Bramley, tend to fruit better on alternate years). Cut out dead wood and the long thin water shoots during the winter months, then get someone experienced to show you how to do the rest of the pruning for it can vary from tree to tree. Alternatively, get a good book on pruning or go on a pruning course.

If the fruit has shown signs of disease take appropriate action. I inherited an enormous Bramley apple tree, but the fruit were badly infested with codling moth. Several years later after pruning and putting a grease band around the trunk to deter pests, it was fruiting much more successfully.

Selling produce

If there is a local demand, surplus produce can be sold at the farmgate. You will need good, accurate scales to ensure that the claimed weights are correct. On a bigger scale, it may be appropriate to register as an organic producer to grow organic crops, as long as there is an assured local market.

Earthworms

Earthworms are an essential part of an organic growing system. Their activities convert plant waste on the surface to wormcasts that are rich in nutrients and minerals and vital for healthy plant growth. Their constant movement also provides drainage channels in the soil.

There are many different species of worms including the common earthworm normally found in the garden and the small red manure worm that thrives in compost heaps and manure piles. Manure worms can be bought, together with a worm composter to generate a constant supply of worm compost, a vital component of home made seed and potting compost. A bought in composter consists of a dustbin shaped container with a tap or drainage holes at the bottom to remove excess moisture. There is a lightweight inner lid that rests on the top of the compost and an overall lid to exclude the light. It is not a sophisticated construction and can be made from existing material at home.

Begin by putting in a little vegetable matter and damp torn up newspaper, add the manure worms then a little more vegetable peelings. Cover, put on the lid and leave them to it for a week or two and check. If much of the vegetable matter has disappeared, sprinkle some more on the surface, cover and wait again. This can be done periodically, and as the number of worms increases so does their appetite. Lightly water occasionally to keep everything damp and after a while add a little lime to maintain the pH balance of the compost. The food given to the worms can be fruit and vegetable peelings, teabags, coffee grounds and sometimes broken up eggshells. Exclude citrus fruit which is too acidic and meat and fish scraps. The wormery needs to function in a temperature range of 10-25°C so may need to be moved to temperate quarters during the winter months. Over time the level in the wormery will rise and it will be necessary to remove the wormcasts below.

Some composters are built in layers so that the top section that includes the worms near the surface can be lifted off and the lower part with the wormcasts can be removed. The top section then becomes the bottom section and the procedure continues. If you haven't got such a system, just remove the top layer which includes the worms, and separate them from the compost. Now replace the worms in a new top layer.

Like many smallholding activities, the breeding of earthworms can be enlarged in scale to become a mini business, supplying others with different worms and wormcasts.

Summary

Requirements:

☐☐☺☺☺☙☙☙£

Space: This depends on the scale of growing activities. A large kitchen garden area with soft fruit bushes and a mini-orchard could easily take up half an acre or 2,000 square metres (50m x 40m).

Time: This is probably the most time consuming activity on the smallholding with a never-ending list of jobs to be done all year round.

Energy: There is plenty of demand on energy resources with so much to do

A small wormery showing the top section where food is provided and the bottom where worm casts are collected. *(Wiggly Wigglers)*

during the summer months. The heavier work of digging and adding manure takes place during the cooler months.

Costs: Starting costs can be high if you need to buy in equipment, seeds, plants, and fertiliser, but once the garden and smallholding is established the running costs should be low, with an ample supply of compost and animal manure to maintain the fertility of the soil.

Useful organisations: *Henry Doubleday Research Organisation (HDRA)* at Ryton Organic Gardens. Tel: 024 7630 3517 www.hdra.org.uk

Recommended books: *The Smallholder's Manual* by Katie Thear,
The Organic Garden Book by Geoff Hamilton
The Pruner's Handbook by John Malins.
Worms Eat My Garbage. Appelhof.

The Black Sex-Link is a good egg layer for the smallholding. A cross between the Rhode Island Red and the Barred Plymouth Rock, it is available in various commercial strains such as the Black Rock and Bovans Nera.

A small moveable house for a flock of free-range layers. They are protected from the fox by electric poultry netting seen at the back.

Chickens

*I want there to be no peasant so poor that he is unable
to have a chicken in his pot every Sunday.* (Henry of Navarre. 1589)

One of the best additions to the smallholding is a flock of chickens. They can be kept for fresh eggs or meat, and they are always a pleasure to have around. There are no restrictions on keeping them, no requirement to register, and if you are keeping a small free range flock on a field scale, no planning permission is needed if you use moveable housing. It is also possible to sell surplus eggs, as long as they are not graded into different sizes and are sold only at the farmgate, on a market stall or directly to buyers. If they are sold to a shop for re-sale, or are graded by size, the producer must be registered with the *Egg Marketing Inspectorate* for the area. If you go in for breeding, and have more than 250 birds, you will be required to register and keep records under the *Disease of Poultry Order 1994*. If table birds are slaughtered and dressed for sale, the premises will need to be registered.

Requirements
Chickens need a house and ranging area that is secure from predators and vermin. The foraging area needs to be well fenced to keep out foxes. Either a tall fence 1.8 - 2.1m (6-7ft) high or electric poultry netting can be used for this. The only other requirements are feeders and drinkers. On a small scale, keeping chickens for the first time need not require a large capital outlay, particularly if you don't need to buy a house. With a well fenced area, they do not take up much space, and need only a minimal amount of time and energy to look after them.

Housing
There is a wide choice of poultry housing available. They are advertised in smallholding and poultry magazines. The house needs to be dry, well ventilated and equipped with a perch, pop-hole exit and nest boxes. The latter should be accessible from outside for ease of egg collection. The house should also have a door or roof that can be removed for cleaning out. A droppings board or pit under the perch is desirable for collecting and removing droppings. For garden poultrykeepers there are houses with integral runs, while those operating on a field scale will usually have a free-standing house that can be moved around by means of wheels or skids, with the grazing area being protected against foxes, by means of high fencing or electric netting. Whatever type of run is organised, the ground that the birds range over will suffer if it is over-used for there will be a build-up of harmful parasites.

Rotating available pasture regularly is essential. While the used ground is vacant, it is a good idea to apply lime at about 3oz to the square metre. This helps to counteract the acidity produced by the poultry droppings. The grass can also be raked and, if needed, resown to replace damaged areas.

Breeds

The decision on what breeds to buy depends largely on what is required of the birds. For egg laying, hybrids or commercial first crosses, particularly those developed for free range will be the best choice. To raise your own poultry meat, buy broilers which are heavy table birds bred to come to killing weight quickly. However, if you wish to avoid leg problems as a result of rapid growth, feed a lower protein ration and raise them on free-range so that they get exercise to strengthen their legs. Table hybrids specifically bred for free-range will grow more slowly and are usually the choice of free-range and organic producers.

Many smallholders love the pure breeds and keep some for pleasure and sometimes to breed replacements. However, this will need a cockerel which will crow in the early morning. If you have neighbours nearby this could be a problem as they may object.

Suppliers are easy to find through the pages of smallholding and poultry magazines. *Country Smallholding* has a particularly large selection. For further details on buying, see Page 17.

Management

There are proprietary feed mixes available for chicks, growers and layers including those that are GM free and also organic feeds. Fully grown birds can be given sufficient feed in the morning that they can clear up in 15 to 20 minutes. They can also be given some mixed corn in the late afternoon. This can be strewn around for them to scratch and peck. Chickens also need constant access to grit and clean water. Self-feed feeders can be placed at a distance from the house to encourage full use of the pasture.

Health

Birds moult once a year, usually in late summer, and often cease laying at this time. Check that the feather loss is not affected by lice and mites. Chickens are vulnerable to external attack by lice and mites, and internally by worms. Lice are about 3mm in length and can be seen on the skin when the feathers are parted. Dust the infected area with *Derris* or another proprietary product and repeat seven days later to eliminate any hatchlings.

Red mites hide in crevices of the hen house during the day, then come out at night to feed on the roosting hens. A severe infestation can kill birds

Free-Range Breeds	
Layers	*Table birds*
Calder Ranger	Hubbard-ISA Redbro strains
Speckledy	Sasso colour feather strains
Babcock 380	Euribrid Hybro white slow grower
Lohmann Brown	Poulet Anglais
Lohmann Tradition	Cotswold White
Hisex Ranger	Devon Bronze
Black Rock	Mastergris
Bovans Nera	Coloryield

These are commercial hybrids and crosses that have been developed for the free-range and organic sectors. If pure, traditional breeds are preferred, they should be from utility rather than show strains if production is important. Examples are Rhode Island Red, Light Sussex, Barred Plymouth Rock. There are many other breeds and bantams too numerous to list here. See *British Poultry Standards*.

so they must be kept down as much as possible. If hens seem reluctant to go into their house at night, this is likely to be as a result of mite attack. Spray every crack and crevice with an appropriate product.

There is another mite that burrows into the skin between the scales of the legs. As a result white crusts are formed which push up the scales. Do not try to pull off the crusts as this will tear the skin. With a bad infestation, place the leg in warm soapy water and brush gently down the leg to dislodge the crusts. Treatment to eliminate the mites is to paint *Benzyl benzoate* onto the infected area with a second application a week later. For details of other problems and diseases that can affect chickens consult a specialist book such as *The Chicken Health Handbook*.

Eggs

Collecting fresh eggs from the nestbox is one of the things that make keeping chickens worthwhile, particularly if there are young children in the family. Collect them two or three times a day if possible, so that eggs are not left lying too long. Sometimes a hen may peck an egg, and this can quickly become a bad habit. The original cause may be boredom or a lack of minerals in the diet. Suspending some cabbage leaves for the hens to peck may help to avoid the problem of egg eating.

Every hen has the potential to lay a certain number of eggs during its lifetime and most of them are laid in the first two years. Hybrids have been bred to lay most of their eggs in their first year after which they are disposed of by commercial farms and new layers installed. For the smallholder less dependent on the wholesale market, these birds are well worth keeping as they lay more eggs overall than today's traditional pure breeds.

The decline in the output of the pure breeds during the last 50 years means that there are no satisfactory measurements available today for the number of eggs laid. It all depends on the particular strain.

Egg laying is seasonal, so when the days grow shorter, laying tails off and stops until the spring. To avoid losing production during winter months there are now sophisticated electronic devices which can switch a light on inside the henhouse during the fading light of the evening and again during the early morning. A low output light is sufficient and can be run from a car battery. There is always a demand for fresh eggs. Customers often want free range or organic eggs. They can be sold at the gate without needing any permission, provided that they are ungraded.

The other demand at the present time, is for pure breeds, particularly bantams. Visit the *Poultry Club of Great Britain*'s annual exhibition to see the whole range of options and talk to the breeders. Buy the best breeding stock available and then concentrate on breeding for excellence. Once you start exhibiting and winning with your own strains, you will be in a good position to sell birds. You will need to advertise them in something like the 'Breeders Directory' in *Country Smallholding* magazine.

Table chickens

Commercial table birds (broilers) such as Cobbs are normally housed in large buildings in dim lighting and reach killing weight around 6 weeks. For the smallholder seeking to raise meat birds more humanely, there are a number of slower growing birds suitable for free range that reach killing weight in 12 weeks. There are colour feathered birds and white breeds.

The cheapest option is to purchase them as day olds, but time and expense is needed to rear them under a heat lamp in draughtproof and ratproof conditions. Once off heat they can be placed in a house with a pop hole so that they can range outside. They will still need protection from predators, notably the fox, so they can be reared on grass with strong high fencing or contained within electric netting. An orchard is an ideal setting as the trees provide shade, wind protection and a sense of security.

Chicks need to be reared on chick crumbs for 6-8 weeks then switched to grower's rations. Remember to make all changes gradual, introducing some grower's rations into the crumbs then gradually increasing the proportion. Sudden changes are stressful. The young birds need access to fresh water at all times and a source of insoluble grit. If you plan to rear birds for sale according to *Free Range*, *Freedom Food* or *Organic* standards, ensure that you comply with their requirements in terms of feeding and management. In any case, it is possible to buy chick crumbs without coccidiostats, and there are companies that supply GM-free feeds as well as organic mixtures.

White and coloured feather table birds being reared on free-range.

At 12 weeks the birds should be ready for slaughter weighing 1.8 - 2.3kg (4-5lb). Now come the stages of killing, plucking, gutting and dressing. None of these things are difficult but there is quite a lot of work involved so some outside help may be needed. If dressed birds are sold, welfare, slaughtering and food safety regulations apply. (See *Legislation*)

Summary: ❑❑☺✺£

Space: Most gardens can easily accommodate a few chickens providing eggs for the family. Producing free range or organic eggs requires adherance to legislation and the relevant marketing requirements. In a house, for example, maximum stocking rate is 7 birds per 1 square metre, while on range, it is 1 bird per 10 sq.m for layers and 1 bird per 1 sq.m. for table birds.

Time: Daily checking, feeding, watering and egg collection - 10-15 minutes. Weekly cleaning and possible moving of house - 30 minutes.

Energy: Minimal requirement with a small flock. Ensure that a moveable house can be handled easily.

Costs: The initial costs are for housing, fencing and stock. After that running costs are low. Feed is the main ongoing expense so check that income is sufficient to at least meet the costs.

Useful organisations: *The Poultry Club of Great Britain* Tel: 01205 724081 www.poultryclub.org
Utility Poultry Breeders' Association. Tel: 01746 714411.

Recommended Books: *Starting with Chickens.* Katie Thear.
Free Range Poultry. Katie Thear.
The Chicken Health Handbook. Gail Damerow.

Indian Runner ducks. They tend to move all together as a group.

Good strains of Khaki Campbells are some of the best layers. (*Poultry World*)

Ducks

Four ducks on a pond, a grass bank beyond. (William Allingham. 1888)

Much of the information regarding buying and basic management is the same as for chickens. However there are a number of differences. Ducks are waterfowl and need access to water, ideally for swimming, but certainly for dipping their heads and splashing their feathers. The ideal is to have a flowing stream which will wash away mud and excrement and provide a constant flow of fresh water. If you have a pond this will suffice very well, but it is important not to have too many birds in relation to its size. It also needs a good level of aeration. There are also moveable rigid ponds that are available from specialist suppliers. These are extremely useful because they can be fitted with a hosepipe inlet and outlet.

Ducks can be kept for eggs, for meat or for interest. They are hardy and are useful providers of winter eggs when chickens may have stopped laying. However, they dislike high winds and they appreciate windbreaks.

Housing

Ducks can be housed in a simple chicken house, but they do not need a perch or a pop-hole. Ideally the door should open downwards, providing a ramp for them. A well ventilated shed or barn can also be adapted for them. Provide a nesting area at one side with chopped straw or wood shavings provided. As far as space in the house is concerned, the largest ducks need around 2 square feet (0.19 sq.m) per bird. Other breeds require a little less.

Breeds

Ducks can be divided into domestic and ornamental breeds. Most people keep domestic breeds for eggs, meat or pleasure. The best egg layers are just as prolific as the best hybrid chickens. Two of the best layers are commercial strains of the Khaki Campbell and the white hybrid supplied by *Cherry Valley*, both of which can produce around 300 eggs in their first year. If a pure, traditional breed is preferred, Indian Runners are quite productive, but less so than commercial laying strains.

The Aylesbury is the traditional table duck but has been replaced commercially by hybrid strains. For example, there are fine hybrid table birds based on the Pekin and the Muscovy.

Ornamental ducks are usually kept by those with a natural source of water. Many like the Mandarin or Green Winged Teal are very colourful.

Duck breeds for the smallholding

Layers	Table	Ornamentals *
Kortlang Khaki Campbell	Pekin/Alesbury	Mandarin
Cherry Valley 2000	Cherry Valley SM3	Tufted duck
Traditional Khaki Campbell	Traditional Aylesbury	Common Shoveler
Indian Runner	Barbary/Muscovy	Common Wigeon
		Green Winged Teal

Most of the commercial laying strains are based on the Khaki Campbell and Indian Runner. Commercial table strains are based either on Aylesbury/Pekin crosses or Pekin/Muscovy crosses.

Other popular domestic breeds are:

Heavy - Rouen, Rouen Clair, Saxony, Cayuga, Silver Appleyard, Pommern, Blue Swedish, Shetland.

Light - Abacot Ranger, Crested, Magpie, Welsh Harlequin, Orpington, Bali.

Bantam or Miniature - Call ducks, Black East Indian, Silver bantam, Crested Miniature, Silver Appleyard Miniature.

    * There are many more ornamentals, too numerous to mention here.

Ornamentals are more difficult to keep than the domestic breeds as each breed has differing environmental needs. It is important that any non-native species should be confined and not allowed to escape into the wild, for this would be an offence under the 1981 *Countryside and Wildlife Act*. The ones shown in the table are all native breeds.

Buying

Buy pure breeds of domestic or ornamental ducks from a reputable breeder. These can be found in breeders' directories in smallholding magazines or reached through duck organisations. Buy healthy birds that are lively, bright-eyed and have a healthy sheen to the feathers. Good birds will be alert with strong legs and feet, with no limps. Keep new birds separate from an existing flock for the first ten days after arrival. For ducklings start with starter rations, then a grower feed, followed by a laying ration at point of lay. If duck rations are not available, those for free-range chickens will do.

Ornamental ducks will also take chicken layer's rations, although there are ornamental duck pellets available, some of which are made to float on water. Give ducks a compound feed in the morning and some grain in the afternoon. A small grain feed may be needed as a bribe if they are reluctant to go into their house in the evening. Young birds should not be allowed to be taken into the water by their mothers. Ducklings can be led into water before they have acquired the oil on their feathers to repel moisture and so can catch cold and die.

Pekin/Aylesbury cross

Management
Each day, release the ducks from their house, checking the birds for signs of ill-health as they come out. Collect the eggs and check and renew the litter as needed. Provide fresh water and feed. Periodically clean out the water courses, move the house and check for vermin.

Health
Ensure that the house litter is always dry, replace the drinking water regularly and act immediately against threats from vermin. Watch for mites on ducklings that have not been into water. If necessary worm ducks through their feed during the winter. *Flubenvet* is effective. Look out for eye or nasal discharge, limping, lack of appetite and loss of condition.

Eggs
There is still some prejudice against duck eggs which can make them difficult to sell. However, on a smallholding scale, if they are clean, there should be a demand from local customers. Selling them farther afield or through retailers will require registration with the *Egg Marketing Inspectorate*. Contrary to some old beliefs, ducks can be trained to use clean nest boxes. If the eggs are not clean, it is not permitted to wash them before selling. These should be cleaned, hard-boiled and used at home straight away.

Ducks start laying at 21-26 weeks. Some commercial strains of the Khaki Campbell can lay more than 300 eggs in their first year.

Table ducks

To raise table ducks buy in commercial strains based on the Pekin/Aylesbury cross, or developed Muscovy birds such as the Barbary crosses. These ducks will fatten quickly to a good size and can be raised in an airy barn with access to fresh water and a protected yard or grass paddock during the day. Buy in as day-olds and raise the duckling under heat lamps for the first week. Feed duck starter rations initially, changing to a grower's ration as the birds develop. Organic rations are available. Table ducks should be ready for slaughter from eight weeks old but can be kept longer if required.

Summary
□□☺☺♨♨£

Space: Small numbers are possible to keep in a garden with pond. For larger numbers, stocking densities are as detailed for chickens.

Time: Daily feeding - 10-15 minutes. Weekly house cleaning 30 minutes.

Energy: Minimal, although cleaning and water provision can be a chore.

Costs: Initial costs are for the house, equipment and stock. The house needs to be simple, strong and ratproof. Stock is normally inexpensive.

Organisations: *The British Waterfowl Association* Tel: 01892 740212 www.waterfowl.org
Domestic Waterfowl Club Tel: 01488 638014 www.domestic-waterfowl.co.uk

Recommended Books: *Starting with Ducks* by Katie Thear.
Domestic Ducks by Chris & Mike Ashton.

Chinese goose. A light breed, it lays more eggs than other geese.

Geese

The fault is great in man or woman, who steals the goose from off a common,
But what can plead that man's excuse, who steals a common from the goose.

(Anon. 1821)

Geese are grass eaters like sheep and are not suitable for keeping on a garden scale. They are normally purchased as young birds and grown on to the autumn on range. When the value of the grass as food drops off, the geese that are destined for the table are brought into a confined area and fattened for the Christmas market.

Geese need short new blades of grass, so it is important to prepare the pasture beforehand by cutting it if necessary. They can be given a ration of mixed corn during the afternoon over the summer months. By late September the nutritional value of the grass has declined. In the past geese were killed soon after this for Michaelmas in October. Today, we confine the geese to a barn, yard or pasture close to the house, during the day and fatten them with an appropriate waterfowl ration for around six weeks and slaughter them in late November for the Christmas market.

If you keep geese for pleasure, they mate for life and can live for up to 40 years. Ganders can be aggressive so should be kept away from young children. They make excellent watchdogs, producing a loud noise and behaving aggressively to strangers; a good deterrent against burglars.

Breeds

There are light, medium and heavy breeds of domestic geese, with the first being the best layers, while the heavy breeds are suitable for the table. Many people keep traditional breeds just for pleasure and often exhibit them at shows. Ornamental or wildfowl breeds are often kept by those with a lake.

The principal heavy breeds are the Embden, the Toulouse and African. Medium weight breeds include the Brecon Buff, Buff Back and Pomeranian. Light breeds include the Chinese, Pilgrim, Roman and Sebastopol.

Apart from craftspeople who will buy surplus eggs, there is no market for the eggs. The best layers, like the Chinese, produce 70-80 eggs per season. The best meat birds come from suppliers with a Legarth strain of the Embden breed. They can be bought in during April or May as goslings and will soon go to work on the pasture. Not everyone buys the modern hybrids. Many smallholders like to keep the traditional breeds, and breed their own replacements. As a smallholder, I kept four different breeds over the years, but I never relied on them for an income.

A trio of Toulouse geese with their house in the background.

Buying

Hybrids bought in for fattening can be ordered early in the year from one of the principal breeders, such as *Norfolk Geese* or one of their regional agents. Commercial strains are usually based on the Scandinavian Legarth strains.

An alternative to hybrids is to buy a few pure breeds or first crosses locally. Pure breeds can also be purchased from specialist breeders who are listed in breeders' directories in smallholding magazines or details can be obtained from relevant waterfowl organisations (see below).

Management

When rearing young birds it is best to feed proprietary rations according to the supplier's instructions. Birds fed well in the early weeks will be able to develop to their full potential. At the same time, it is important not to feed rations that are too high in protein otherwise there is a risk of developing conditions such as a dropped wing, where the muscles are unable to hold the wing in the normal position along the body.

Goslings can be raised in the same way as ducks before transferring to grass entirely. Though vigorous grazers, geese will appreciate a grain feed in the afternoon. A little grit should always be available for proper digestion. Neither goslings nor ducklings are safe from predators, particularly rats, so they need to be confined until they are practically fully feathered. All water-

Goose breeds

Heavy	Medium	Light
African	Brecon Buff	Chinese
American Buff	Buff Back	Pilgrim
Embden	Grey Back	Roman
Toulouse	Pomeranian	Sebastopol
	West of England	Shetland
		Steinbacher

Commercial strains	Ornamentals *	
Legarth	Red-Breasted	* These need a
Grey Landes	Barnacle	considerable expanse
	Ne-Ne (Hawaian goose)	of water and are only
	Emperor	appropriate where a
	Bar-Headed	lake is available. Non-
	Lesser White-Fronted	native breeds must be
		kept confined.

fowl need protection from foxes or badgers, so should be kept secure at night. A well ventilated house is needed. On a commercial scale, an open-fronted barn that can be closed off with an open-mesh door at night, is ideal. During the day geese need the same fencing protection as chickens.

Health
Ducks and geese are less likely to have health problems than chickens. With good management, and regular worming once a year, they should be fine. Gizzard worm is a particular threat to young geese. Two other things to look out for are lameness or dropped wings, as referred to earlier. The former can be a strained leg or damaged foot. The foot can be cleaned up and a veterinary spray applied. Keep the patient confined on clean straw for a while before rejoining the flock.

Dropped wings can be taped into place where young birds are concerned, but remove the tape after a week, as the bird is growing quickly. Mature birds with dropped wings will manage alright, but don't breed from them as the trait can be hereditry. There are a number of diseases that can affect geese, but these are dealt with by more specialised books.

Summary
□□□☺🖐£

Space: Geese are grass eaters and need a paddock or orchard to graze . 5-6 breeding geese will need an acre, while those that are being raised for one season only will have a stocking density of 250 per acre. Like ducks they

Grass is the mainstay of the goose's diet. This one is a Legarth strain of commercial Embden.

also need a water source so that they can immerse their heads, as well as a fox-proof house at night. Inside, stocking density is 0.7 - 0.9 sq.m. per bird.

Time: For feeding, paddock and house maintenance, and water tank cleaning, an average of around 1 - 2 hours a week.

Energy: Little energy needed, although ganders can be aggressive in spring. A dustbin lid makes a good shield when entering their space.

Costs: A simple robust house and a water tank that can be topped up with a hose, are the main initial expenditure, apart from the geese themselves. These need not be costly if purchased as goslings. Ongoing costs are low with just an afternoon grain feed. From October when the grass is no longer nutritious, the birds can be brought into a yard with airy barn and will need a higher rate of feeding, particularly those that are being fattened for the Christmas market. The process of catching, killing and plucking will also mean the expense of extra labour. Hopefully sales will recoup the expenses with some profit at the end.

Useful organisations: *The British Waterfowl Association* Tel: 01892 740212 www.waterfowl.org
Domestic Waterfowl Club Tel: 01488 638014 (evenings) www.domestic-waterfowl.co.uk
The Goose Club Tel: 01437 563308 www.gooseclub.org.uk

Recommended Books: *Starting with Geese* by Katie Thear.

Turkeys

It was a turkey. He could never have stood upon his legs, that bird.

(A Christmas Carol. Charles Dickens. 1843)

If you have a large barn or outhouse, you have potential premises for raising turkeys. There should be plenty of light and air, and enough room for the turkeys to grow. Above all, it needs to be secure against foxes.

Turkeys should be kept separately from other poultry as they are vulnerable to protozoan infections such as Blackhead (Histomoniasis) and Coccidiosis, although ensuring that they only have access to clean, well-drained pasture minimises the risk. They can go out into a run by day provided that it is securely fenced aganst foxes and protected from the wind. Outside perches are popular. Inside, straw bales make good perching areas.

Breeds

There is a choice from a range of different-sized hybrid breeds or slower-growing traditional coloured breeds. The most popular of these are the Bronze and the Norfolk Black. There are other breeds available, including the black and white Cröllwitzer, Slate, Buff and Bourbon Red. Specialist breeders can be found in breeders' directories in smallholding magazines or by contacting the appropriate organisations. Local hybrid agents can usually be found in *Yellow Pages*.

Buying

Buy poults at six weeks old in the summer and keep them on 3 inches (8cm) of woodshavings or clean chopped straw in a confined building which ideally has plenty of light and fresh air. Poults are normally sold 'as hatched' (AH) so there will be a mixture of males and females. The males (stags) grow larger so take that into consideration when planning your sales. If bought at a younger age, the poults will need a heated environment.

Management

Food and water should be provided with suspended feeders and drinkers which can be raised as the birds grow. Begin with starter crumbs, then move onto grower's pellets and end with finisher pellets, following the manufacturer's guidelines. There is a range of high protein turkey rations, most of which include coccidiostats to prevent disease, but it is possible to buy the additive-free, if preferred.

Turkey breeds

Traditional breeds: Norfolk Black, Bronze, Cambridge Bronze
Black-Winged Bronze, British White, Buff
Bourbon Red, Slate, Cröllwitzer, Pied.

Commercial breeds: Commercial Bronze, Beltsville Small White. *

* There are many other commercial, white-feathered strains but these often grow too big for the average oven and are best avoided.

When entering their quarters, do so slowly and quietly as turkeys panic easily and may damage their wingtips. After a time they will get used to comings and goings, especially if the same person feeds them every day.

The smallholder raising a relatively small number of turkeys may be able to sell them direct to the public, thus maximising the profit. Discerning buyers are interested in quality. Bronze turkeys with a more traditional shape and more gamey flavour are popular. The Commercial Bronze was produced by crossing the traditional Bronze with commercial hybrid strains. It is possible to purchase entirely organic rations and offer the finished product as an organically reared bird, which can be sold at a premium.

Leave sufficient time to kill and pluck the birds. Withdraw all feed 12 hours before slaughter but leave them with water. Help will be needed whether hand pluckers are called in or a small plucking machine is used. Once plucked and eviscerated the turkeys can be hung in a cold place for up to ten days before trussing and putting in a cold store ready for the customers. Welfare, slaughtering and food safety regulations will apply.

Don't neglect advertising locally several months beforehand. It is important to give customers the size of bird that they ordered, or they may not come back next year.

Health
Reference has already been made to Blackhead and Coccidiosis. Turkeys are also vulnerable to parasitic worms, so if they are let out regularly, rotate the grass area to minimise the risk. Don't let turkeys out onto long, damp grass, nor in the rain or windy conditions.

Summary
❑❑☺🖐££

Space: Inside the house, one square metre for every three birds is needed. Outside, the maximum stocking density is 800 birds per hectare (2.5 acres).

Bronze male turkey displayimg.

Time: Daily feeding, watering and checking the birds - 30 minutes. Weekly cleaning - 30 to 60 minutes. If rearing birds for Christmas, there are three weeks of work at the end.

Energy: Minimal output until Nov/Dec when those birds for the Christmas market need to be caught, killed and plucked. This is hard work!

Costs: Without a suitable building already on site, it is probably not worth keeping turkeys. Initial costs are the birds, and feeders and drinkers. Ongoing costs are for feeds and bedding. Turkeys grow rapidly and feed costs will expand with the birds. Killing and plucking means the extra cost of additional labour at the time. Hopefully Christmas sales will cover all the cost and bring a profit.

Useful Organisations:
Turkey Club UK. Tel: 01223 262484. www.turkeyclub.org.uk

Recommended books
The Smallholder's Manual. Katie Thear
Turkeys: A Guide to Management. David Bland.

Guinea Fowl

At first sight, the Guinea fowl looks out of proportion, with its round body and tiny head. (The Smallholder's Manual. Katie Thear. 2002)

Guinea fowl originate from west Africa. They have a small head for their size and are inclined to be flighty, ranging over a wide area and perching on fences, roofs and in trees. They are noisy and excitable and give loud shrieking calls. This means that they are suitable as watchdogs on a farm or smallholding which has no close neighbours. Much of their food comes from insects so they need little supplementary feeding. They are ideal in orchards where they help to keep down the incidence of insect pests. During the winter months they will be glad of the protection of a barn or outhouse, particularly if there is a fairly high perch.

Breeds
There are no breed standards for guinea fowl but there is a range of colours. The most common colour is the pearl which is a grey with white dots. There are also white, lavender and mulberry (purple) variations.

Management
Where insects make up a good proportion of the diet, a daily feed of mixed grain will suffice, but this needs to be fine as the crop is small. A mixed bird mixture is suitable if there are only a few birds kept. On a more commercial scale, purpose-made proprietary feeds are available. Providing grit to help grain digestion is recommended.

Ranging birds will start laying in the spring usually under a hedge somewhere. If there are also male birds among the flock, the hens will go broody after laying around 20 eggs. These can be collected and incubated over 28 days although as the shells are thick they are difficult to candle. Removing them on a regular basis from the nest will ensure that the hen goes on laying, as many as 100 eggs in a season.

Guinea Fowl can also be raised commercially as meat birds. They will need to be raised in a barn with good ventilation in the same way as turkeys. They are popular with hotels and restaurants, but it is essential to check that there is a market there before undertaking such an enterprise. If selling through a third party, registration is required and welfare, slaughter and food safety regulations apply.

Guinea fowl are excellent 'watchdogs' and insect controllers. The one at the back is a Lavender and the one at the front is a Pearl.

Health

Ranging birds are very hardy and are unlikely to suffer from health problems. They should be wormed once a year in late summer with *Flubenvet* included in their feed. They can also be checked and treated for external parasites at the same time.

Summary
❑ ☺ ✍ £

Space: Guinea fowl are not for small areas because they are very noisy and are bound to upset close neighbours. They need trees to roost in but when the weather is severe will be glad of the shelter of a barn. On a larger scale, the stocking rates are the same as for chickens.

Time: Feeding daily and checking their water can be done in a few minutes.

Energy: There is almost nothing to do on a daily basis. Raising chicks and slaughtering are more time and energy consuming.

Costs: Initial cost is for the birds, unless it is a commercial enterprise. Thereafter there is just the daily feeding and general care.

Recommended books: *Guineafowl Past and Present.* Michael Roberts.

Quail

The quails whistle about us their spontaneous cries.
(Wallace Stevens. 1923)

You do not need to be a smallholder to keep a few quail. These small birds can be kept in a shed or small poultry house. Like other poultry, quail are kept for pleasure, for eggs or for meat. Raising quail for meat is a specialised operation not practical on a small scale. Keeping them for eggs is worth doing, as is collecting and breeding the different breeds and colours as a hobby. The profit from producing quail eggs is not large but it can make a useful contribution to the smallholder's overall income. It is possible to buy clear plastic quail egg boxes that hold a dozen eggs. The surplus can be sold primarily to local customers.

Breeds

Keeping quail for eggs or meat means buying in good commercial Coturnix stock. Beyond this there are many coloured variations of Coturnix kept by hobbyists, and the smaller but pretty Chinese Painted quail. The American Bobwhite is a large quail from the USA, originally bred as a commercial bird but superseded today by the Coturnix, and again, kept just by hobbyists in the UK. The tiny Chinese Painted or Button quail are for hobbyists only, and they are often kept in aviaries. Breeders of all types of quail can be found through the breeder's directories of smallholding magazines.

Management

Quail can be housed in large cages, pens or an aviary. Although they are ground birds, they will fly straight up if frightened and can disappear over the highest fence. The top of the run must therefore be covered. An inner soft netting under the roof will prevent them banging their heads.

They need protection from predators, mostly cats and rats, so their housing must be secure. They can be kept inside a shed, barn or outhouse most of the year. In summer they can be put into a moveable run on grass during the day and brought back at night. If you have an aviary, some quail can be introduced. As ground birds they will scavenge, pecking up seeds that have been dropped by flying birds.

Feeding

Young quail can be fed proprietary chick crumbs which have the high proportion of protein that they need. Use the coccidiostat-free crumbs if you

Varieties of the Coturnix quail are the best layers.

can get them. Once the birds are grown, purpose-produced quail layer's pellets can be fed. These are made to a small size suitable for quail to eat. If you cannot buy them locally, it is possible to produce your own mixture, as follows: one part chick crumbs(coccidiostat free), one part canary seed and one part millet. You can also offer them surplus lettuce leaves or the outer leaves from other garden vegetables. They also need access to grit and fresh water at all times.

Breeding

Quail come into lay after about 5-6 weeks and can be fertile a week or two later, so it is already time to think about breeding replacements. Although it is possible to buy in replacement laying stock, most people like to breed their own.

49

Breeds of Quail

Production *	Interest
Japanese Coturnix	Chinese Painted (Button) *
Italian Coturnix	Bobwhite
American Range Coturnix	
English White Coturnix	* There are many different strains of the Coturnix laying quail, as well as a variety of colours, as shown. They are all good layers.
Tuxedo Coturnix	
Fawn Coturnix	
Manchurian Gold Coturnix	** There are many different colour varieties of the small Chinese Painted Quail eg, Silver, White, Fawn, Pearl, Black, Ivory, etc.

Select the breeding stock carefully and house 5 or 6 females with a suitable male. Discard the eggs for the first couple of days then collect them each day for incubation. Keep them in a cool place until there are sufficient, then put them into an incubator which has been set up ready. (See next chapter).

Newly hatched quail are very small, not much larger than a bumble bee. They need constant warmth as well as access to food and water, together with protection from draughts and rats. As with all newly hatched birds, put out a water container with pebbles in to prevent the bird falling in and drowning. Chick crumbs may be too large for the tiny newly hatched birds, so they may need to be crushed. Between three and six weeks old it should be possible to sex the chicks as the males will be growing larger and heavier, and the breast will be reddish in colour.

Eggs

Quail's eggs are a luxury item and should find a ready market at the farm gate. Beyond this, they can be offered to delicatessens and restaurants. However, the producer will need to be registered for this.

Summary

☐ ☺ ✋ £

Space: Quail need little space and can utilise existing available space, either in an aviary, or in hutches or cages, in a shed or outhouse.

Time: Feeding, watering and egg collecting can take about 15 minutes daily unless there are large numbers. Periodically they need cleaning out.

Energy: Minimal outlay needed for these little birds.

Costs: Cages and birds are the main capital costs. Feed costs are very low.

Recommended books:

Keeping Quail by Katie Thear (Fourth edition due in 2005)

Breeding Replacement Poultry

One of the chief objects during the spring months is to hatch and rear pullets to replace the old hens. (Herbert Howes. 1930)

There are two ways of incubating eggs; the natural way with a broody mother hen or by using an incubator. In many respects a broody hen is ideal as she instinctively knows what to do and after hatching will prove to be a good mother to her chicks. Once she has settled in as a broody it is necessary to provide food and water close by and install some protection against rats and foxes. If she should go broody under a hedge or another place that cannot be fully protected, it is worth preparing a broody coop and run and installing her there on a clean straw nest with her eggs. She may lose interest but if she is really broody, she can be moved and will settle on a given clutch of eggs. I used to have a neighbour who would ring up in the spring to ask *"Has that hen of yours gone broody yet"*? If she had, and we didn't need her services, he would come round with a dozen fertile eggs from his pure breed hens and settle her down with them.

A good broody will sit on duck eggs, as well. When they hatch she will be just as good a mother with her new hatchlings as she would with chicks.

Our broody hen was a bantam cross. Bantams are often good broodies as are Silkies and Silkie crosses but the disadvantages of relying solely on broodies is that birds can go broody when you don't need them and fail to do so when you really do. Although hens are normally reliable, they can abandon their eggs at any stage, particularly if they have been frightened by a dog, other animals or boisterous children. Broody hens need a quiet place where they won't be disturbed. Another factor arises with a growing flock of birds, producing more and more fertile eggs and not having sufficient broodies available. This is when you need an incubator.

Artificial incubation

If you are likely to have a regular need for incubating eggs, an incubator will prove to be a good investment. A second hand incubator is probably not a good idea unless you can satisfy yourself that it works perfectly. A new incubator will have solid state electronic controls that set the correct temperatures and humidity and will turn the eggs regularly just like the mother hen. Buy an incubator that has a greater capacity than you need initially as inevitably one's requirements increase and in a year or two you will be glad of the extra space.

Incubation Chart

	Incubating	Pipping	Hatching
Chickens	Day 1 - 18. Temp: 37.5°C Humidity: 52%	Day 18. Temp: 37°C Humidity: 75%	Day 21. Temp: 37°C Humidity: 75%
Ducks	Day 1 - 25. Temp: 37.5°C Humidity: 58%	Day 25. Temp: 37°C Humidity: 75%	Day 28. Temp: 37°C Humidity: 75%
Geese	Day 1 - 28. Temp: 37.5°C Humidity: 55%	Day 28. Temp: 37°C Humidity: 75%	Day 31. Temp: 37°C Humidity: 75%
Turkeys	Day 1 - 25. Temp: 37.5°C Humidity: 55%	Day 25. Temp: 37°C Humidity: 75%	Day 28. Temp: 37°C Humidity: 75%
Guinea Fowl	Day 1 - 25. Temp: 37.5°C Humidity: 55%	Day 25. Temp: 37°C Humidity: 75%	Day 28. Temp: 37°C Humidity: 75%
Quail	Day 1 - 15. Temp: 37.5°C Humidity: 45%	Day 15. Temp: 37°C Humidity: 75%	Day 18. Temp: 37°C Humidity: 75%

Average hatching times shown. Heavy breeds may take slightly longer.

Site the incubator indoors, in a spare bedroom, for example, where the outside temperature and humidity do not fluctuate too much, then follow the manufacturer's instructions to the letter. The incubator must be scrupulously cleaned before use so that it is free of pathogens that could affect the eggs. Run it empty for at least 24 hours to ensure that everything is working.

Incubate only well shaped eggs without cracks or shell defects. Eggs that are dirty should be cleaned with a brush then washed in hand-warm water with added egg sanitant before being placed in the incubator. Incubate them as soon as possible and bring them to room temperature for a day before putting them in the incubator.

When they have been incubating for a week remove them one by one and hold each egg in front of a bright light bulb so that you can see inside. The developing embryo should look rather like a spider with a dark centre spot and strands radiating from it. Any egg that does not have this pattern, and that looks clear, should be discarded for it is not fertile.

After 18 days (for chickens) the eggs will begin to pip where the chick's beak breaks through the shell. (See the table above for other species). Now egg turning ceases and the chicks should emerge over the next three days. The new born chicks can be left to dry out and fluff up for a day then moved to a secure place under a dull emitter heat lamp and provided with chick crumbs and water. A small shallow bowl filled with stones and topped up with water is suitable so that the chicks can't drown.

Finally, remove all the shells and clean and disinfect the incubator ready for the next batch. The incubator can be used for game and waterfowl eggs too in which case the manufacturer's instructions should always be followed.

Young birds in a protected brooding area.

Hatching successes can be maximised by ensuring the following:
• Select breeding stock carefully. They should be in excellent health and good examples of their type. Indiscriminate breeding should be avoided.
• Unless it is unavoidable, do not mate birds that are too closely related for there is an increased risk of genetic defects in the chicks.
• Feed the breeding birds on a proprietary breeder's ration so that there is less risk of deficiency diseases such as rickets in the chicks.
• Try to avoid incubating eggs that are more than a week old.
• Choose eggs carefully and wash them with an egg sanitant to minimise diseases in the developing embryo.
• Use a modern incubator with electronic and egg turning controls.
• Follow the manufacturer's instructions with regard to temperature and humidity settings and controls.
• Have the incubator in an area where the temperature and humidity do not fluctuate, and where it is unlikely to be knocked.

Summary

Space, time, energy and cost requirements are entirely dependent on the scale of operations and on the degree of interest of the poulty keeper. Once the incubator is bought, and a brooding area set up, running costs are low.
Recommended book: *Incubation*. Katie Thear.

Rabbits

A great amount of mental relaxation can be derived from the keeping of rabbits.
(J C Sandford)

Rabbits are quiet animals that are easy to keep and are popular with children. Their needs are for fresh air, exercise, protection from predators, and adequate food and water. They can be kept indoors, in a shed or with quarters outside which are protected from bad weather.

Breeds
Most breeds are kept as pets or for showing. These include the lop breeds, Rex breeds, Dutch and many more. There are also heavy fast growing breeds kept for meat, such as the Californian or the New Zealand White. Finally there are Angora rabbits kept for their fine wool.

Management
Most rabbits are kept in a hutch consisting of an exercise section that is open to the light and air, and separate sleeping quarters. Meat producers sometimes keep them in cages so that the droppings fall through the floor. These are not satisfactory from the welfare point of view, for the rabbits can suffer from sore hocks. Cages are also associated with intensive farming.

The RSPCA welfare guidelines specify an overall area for one rabbit to be 20sq ft (1.9sq m) and 54 sq ft (5 sq m) for two rabbits. The housing needs to be airy but fully weatherproof. There are indoor hutches designed for placing in a shed or barn and outside ones that are of a heavier construction to cope with the weather.

During the summer months, rabbits enjoy being on the grass during the day and a suitable house and run can be provided. Wherever they are kept, regular cleaning out and replacement of chopped straw litter is essential. Water is best provided with a nipple drinker attached to the front netting.

Rabbits need a balanced diet of a proprietary cereal mix or pellets and roughage in the form of hay and vegetables. Fresh greens from the kitchen garden are suitable, while carrots are popular for gnawing and keeping the teeth in good order.

Breeding
It is well known that rabbits breed quickly. A doe can have up to six litters a year, although non-commercial smallholders will normally opt for less. If mating is required, the doe should be introduced into the buck's quarters, never the other way round or there will be fighting.

Californian rabbit, an attractive breed with white fur and chocolate brown or black markings.

Pregnancy lasts for an average of 31 days. For the first three and a half weeks, the doe should continue with her normal ration of proprietary pellets or cereal mix and hay, but after this, the ration should be increased to cater for her forthcoming lactation.

A few days before giving birth (kindling) she will begin to make a nest in the sleeping compartment, often pulling out some of her soft fur to line it. She is best left alone during this period and also while she is giving birth.

The young rabbits are pink and hairless at birth, and their eyes are closed., but they develop quite quickly and will soon want to leave the nest. The doe will feed them until they are about 7 weeks old. Before this, they will have begun to eat solid food and hay. Once weaned, they can be separated from the mother and by the time they are 10 weeks old, the sexes should also be separated from each other.

Health
Breeding stock and pet rabbits should be vaccinated against the lethal conditions of myxomatosis and rabbit haemorrhagic virus disease (RHVD). A vet will normally do this when the animals are 6 weeks old.

Breeds of Rabbits

Table	Fibre and Skins	Pets and Fancy
New Zealand White	Angora	Lops
Hybrid White	Chinchilla	Netherlands Dwarf
Californian	Sable	Rex
		British Giant
		Satins, etc *

* There are many other breeds and varieties.
Table and fibre breeds are also kept as pets.

Dry, well ventilated and clean housing will go a long way to keeping the rabbits healthy and free of colds (snuffles), as well as Coccidiosis and Pasteurellosis which can be treated with antibiotics. A good, balanced diet with hay and not too many greens will prevent digestive upsets such as the 'blows', where gas collects in the system.

The ears should be checked for the presence of mites, indicated by an orange coloured deposit in the ear passages. Veterinary ear canker drops are available for this condition. Mange mites and fleas are other external parasites that may appear. Carry out regular checks and treat with an appropriate product obtainable from the vet or registered animal supplier.

Unless the rabbits have regular outside exercise, the claws will need to be clipped, otherwise they will grow too long. Angora rabbits will need regular grooming and clipping to prevent the coat becoming matted.

Finally, all newly kindled does should be checked for sore, inflamed teats, in case it leads to mastitis. Again, an antibiotic can be used to treat this.

Summary
□☺☺✋£

Space: Rabbits need very little space unless you intend to keep meat rabbits on a large scale. This is not advisable at present, as there is little profit in it.

Time: Relatively short, just to check food and water twice daily, examine the rabbits and clean out the housing twice weekly. More time will be needed for putting them out for exercise, and where breeding takes place on a regular basis. Angora rabbits also take up more time with regular grooming.

Energy: On a small scale, minimal once the housing has been set up.

Costs: Again, but depending on the scale, very little as stock, housing, equipment and supplies are not expensive.

Organisations: *The British Rabbit Council*. Tel: 01636 676042. www.thebrc.org
The British Commercial Rabbit Association. Tel: 01270 780248.

Recommended books: *The Rabbit Handbook*. Karen Gendron.
The Domestic Rabbit. Sandford.

Bees

A land flowing with milk and honey (The Bible)

Keeping bees can be a good part of the range of smallholding activities. There are no restrictions, although the beekeeper is expected not to put others at risk through poor siting of hives and there are procedures to be followed concerning disease control and prevention. Apart from the absorbing interest in bees as a hobby, there is the annual bonus of the honey harvest and beeswax, and good pollination levels for fruit trees and crops. If honey is sold there are regulations in relation to quantities, labelling and food safety. See *Legislation*. The following are the salient points in relation to beekeeping, but it is essential to learn by practical experience, and this usually comes from other beekeepers.

• Join the local beekeeping association. The local library will have details.
• Try and 'apprentice' yourself to a local beekeeper who can take you through the different aspects and stages of the craft.
• Read relevant books. If the library does not have a good selection of bee books, they will always order them in for you, but you may have to wait a few weeks. The best and most clearly written beginner's book is *Starting with Bees* by Peter Gordon.
• Ideally, go on a beekeeping course. The *British Beekeepers' Association* organises some and there are others run by local societies. Beekeeping equipment suppliers often have courses, as well as some agricultural colleges.
• Most of the activities in the beekeeper's year take place between April and September, so Spring is the ideal time to begin.
• Start with a nucleus of bees (a few frames with mated queen bee and attendant workers) and a couple of hives. These and all the other equipment, such as bee veil, smoker and hive tool are available from bee suppliers. It is also possible to acquire hives, equipment and bee colonies through the local association, but make sure that anything secondhand is thoroughly cleaned to avoid introducing disease.
• A nucleus of bees from a commercial supplier will be free of disease. They will have been treated against Varroa mites, using methods approved by *DEFRA*.
• Site the hives so that they face away from where people are likely to be walking. Avoid positions under trees or where it is windy.
• The advantage of starting with a small nucleus is that the colony grows at the same rate as the new beekeeper's experience. Add new brood frames to the brood chamber of the hive so that there is plenty of room for the queen to lay her eggs. It may be necessary to feed some sugar syrup (1kg white

granulated sugar to 1 litre of water) or sugar candy from bee suppliers.

• Check the hive about once a week to ten days. If bees are actively working to bring in pollen and nectar, the queen is almost certainly present and actively laying eggs.

• Provide a source of shallow water with stones in it, so that the bees can get water nearby without drowning.

• Towards the end of April, put a queen excluder on top of the brood chamber, then add a super with foundation frames so that honey can be stored. The queen excluder stops the queen going up into the super frames to lay eggs there, but the worker bees are able to get through.

• In June the field beans, white clover and lime tree blossom become available. If the bees have been visiting oilseed rape fields, remove the frames and honey straight away as it sets rapidly.

• Watch for signs of swarming and take action to avoid it by making sure there is enough room in the brood box for egg laying. Remove unwanted queen cells. Put on more supers, as needed.

• In August and September, remove the honey frames and extract the honey with an extractor. This is an expensive item but can sometimes be borrowed from the local bee group.

• Treat for Varroa as soon as the last honey has been extracted.

• Feed the bees with sugar syrup so that they can build up enough stores to see them through the winter.

• Put a mouse guard on the entrance and when winter comes, leave the bees alone for they are clustered in a ball inside the hive, keeping warm.

Summary

☐☺✋✋££

Space: Beekeeping takes up very little space, unless the hobby takes hold and the number of hives grows. In that situation, many will be sited elsewhere, to take advantage of the oilseed rape or heather on the moors.

Time: From October to February there is little to do. Activities build up as the colony grows through the summer. Expect to spend about 30 minutes/ week during the summer period, plus the time spent extracting the honey.

Energy: Minimal with three exceptions - relocating hives, chasing a swarm and moving heavy supers for the honey harvest.

Costs: Setting up costs are high, even with some secondhand equipment. The running costs are minimal.

Organisations: *British Beekeepers' Association (BBKA)*. Tel: 02476 696679. www.bbka.org.uk

Recommended books: *Starting with Bees*. Peter Gordon.
Bees at the Bottom of the Garden. Alan Campion.

Pigs

Dogs look up to you, cats look down at you,
but pigs treat you as an equal. (Anon)

Everyone likes pigs for they are intelligent responsive animals. They can be bred for profit or raised for meat, and on a small scale this can be done with little land. A couple of weaners can be raised with just a sty and concrete run, taking up no more than 30 square metres overall.

They will fatten readily, particularly if there is surplus whey available from dairying operations. Weaners can be bought at 3-8 weeks old and reared for 4-6 months to slaughter weight. If keeping pigs is a new venture, prepare first by reading specialist publications and, if possible, attend a course. To keep pigs it is necessary to be registered. For this and other regulations involved in pig keeping, see *Legislation*.

Breeds

Select a breed according to your requirements. To produce pork at the least cost may be one consideration, choosing a breed that is sweet natured another, or keeping a rare breed and selling weaners could be yet another. The modern hybrid pigs have been developed long and lean with a lower proportion of fat to meat, but they are less suitable for outside conditions.

Pigs are kept for pork or slaughtered later as bacon pigs. Some breeds become fatty above a certain age and are unsuitable as baconers. Many smallholders keep traditional breeds. If they come from a good line, the young can be sold to other smallholders, as potential breeding stock. They can also be crossed with more modern breeds to produce good quality porkers.

Berkshire: This is a medium weight black pork pig that matures quickly.
British Lop: A quite rare, long and white bacon pig, this is a good grazer and has the reputation for being a good mother.
British Saddleback: Developed from the Essex and Wessex Saddlebacks, this is black with a white band across the shoulders and extending down to the forelegs. It is a hardy pig that is widely used for cross breeding.
Duroc: This is a long, lean, commercial ginger pig that is also hardy.
Gloucester Old Spots: Known as the cottager's pig, this was kept in the orchards of the west country. It is white with black spots, and is a big hardy pig, suitable for pork or bacon, but slow growing.
Kunekune: A small, hairy and patchy pig from New Zealand, this is fast growing for pork, and is ready from the age of 5 months.
Large Black: This is a large, hardy and docile bacon pig, but grows slowly.

Berkshire pig in an outdoor concrete run attached to a house. The sturdy metal post and wire fence separates it from the next-door run.

Saddleback pig in front of its sty.

Large White: A pork or bacon breed, this is often used for cross breeding.

Middle White: This is a quick growing docile pork pig, ready from 16 weeks.

Oxford Sandy and Black: A docile, patchy pig suitable for pork or bacon.

Tamworth: This is an ancient and hardy ginger pig with a long snout. It is great for turning over the soil but is a very fast runner. It is a slow maturing pork pig which can be kept to bacon weight. It is often used for crossing, particularly with wild boar.

Vietnamese Pot Bellied: This hardy little, black pork pig can be bred at 6 months, and is ready for slaughter soon afterwards.

Welsh: A docile, commercial white pig, this is suitable for pork or bacon. It is often used for crossing with other breeds.

Management

Pig breeders may be found locally or in the breeder's directory section of smallholding magazines. Novices should avoid markets and ensure that animals are seen before purchase. A healthy pig is easy to recognise. (See Page 17). Whatever scale of pigkeeping is undertaken, a pig house or sty with an attached exercise area is needed. It can be used at the outset whilst gaining experience, for winter quarters, for farrowing or for keeping a boar. The house and surrounding wall should be constructed of blocks with a strong heavy gate. Pigs are strong animals and will seek out weak points.

The roof needs to be well insulated and the flooring throughout should be of concrete, combed to prevent slipping and with a drainage channel and outlet at the end of the run so that the water from rain and hosing down will run away from the house. With a thick layer of straw in the house, pigs will be comfortable there even during harsh winter weather.

With pasture available, pigs can be put out to graze. They will need a simple field shelter for protection from the weather. Field arks or moveable houses can be bought or easily constructed. A house with straw inside as bedding, should be placed with the entrance on the leeward side, and be free of draughts. Pigs need access to fresh water at all times. Some will root more than others, ripping up the pasture. Pigs are excellent as ploughs, turning over the ground and crunching up weed roots. (See page 22).

Strong fencing is necessary to keep pigs in, using either pig netting or two strands of electric wire at 10cms (4 inches) and 40cms (16 inches) height. Keep the grass around the perimeter short to avoid contact with the lower wire. Electric fencing can also be used to provide access to different areas of the field so that the pasture is used in rotation.

Food and water should be provided in strong heavy containers that cannot be readily turned over. Proprietary rations can be fed according to age. This is the biggest ongoing expense. To reduce this outlay it is possible to

A moveable house for pigs on pasture.

make a grower's ration as follows: 10 parts coarse wholemeal, 8 parts barley meal, 1 part soya meal, 1 part fishmeal plus minerals.

For breeding stock taken through the winter months, fodder crops can be grown. Examples are potatoes (feed cooked), Jerusalem artichokes, carrots, beet, parsnips, turnips and swedes. Brassicas are also popular. Swill should never be given. It is against the law to do so.

Farrowing and raising young

A sow will first come on heat between 6 -7 months old. She can then be put to an unrelated boar. He can be of the same breed, or a different one to produce crossbred weaners that are more profitable. They finish more quickly or produce more or leaner meat in a given time. When breeding for good purebred stock it may be more convenient to use artificial insemination. No pigs need to be moved and the semen will be from a high quality boar.

Prepare an area for the piglets with a heat lamp. This is adjacent to the mother, but separated by a steel bar so that she cannot roll over and squash them. At birth, check each piglet carefully and ensure that the airways are free from mucous. Place each new one in a box beneath the lamp until the process is all over. The last stage is when the afterbirth is discharged. Put each of the new piglets close to a teat to encourage them to take their first feed. The first milk is colostrum and is rich in nutrients. Antibodies are also passed through it to the young. These help them cope with infections.

After two weeks the young will be ready for a beginner's ration. Weaning time is around 8 weeks. After the birth, the sow needs to be fed normal rations for the first two days, then have it increased to 2kg (4lb) a day, plus

Tamworth sow with piglets. The crush bar behind provides a protected area under a heat lamp in case the piglets are crushed

0.25kg (0.5lb) for each piglet she is suckling. Try to get the new family out of the shed and onto the pasture as soon as the piglets are sufficiently hardy. After the weaners have been removed from the mother, they need to be fed twice a day. Provide just enough that they can clear up in 20 minutes.

Health

A healthy pig will have bright eyes, and a cold, not runny nose. The coat should be smooth and silky and the tail curly. She should also have a good appetite and come forward at feeding time without limping. Any variation in these factors should be checked. You can take her temperature by inserting the thermometer in the rectum. Normal temperature is 38.6 - 38.8°C. If it is higher, isolate the pig and contact the vet.

In the summer, pigs are vulnerable to sunburn and heat stress, so they always need a shady area. The ideal is to provide a wallow, which is a shallow water area for them to cool down. Pigs also need to be wormed regularly. Treat adult pigs every 4 - 6 months with *Invermectin*. Treat sows at weaning time, then again three weeks before farrowing. The essential vaccination for pigs is against Erysipelas. Pregnant sows and gilts must be done at least three weeks before farrowing. Vaccinate young stock according to the manufacturer's instructions. Pigs are also subject to skin parasites, mange and lice. Inject pigs twice a year with *Ivomec* or *Dectomex* to prevent the condition. If a pig needs to be moved off site for any reason, a movement licence from the local *Animal Health Office* is needed.

Electric fencing is very effective in confining these Gloucester Old Spots to a specific area.

Selling

Selling newly weaned stock is desirable as the outlay on each animal has been minimal. Ensure that you produce pigs that others want. Bringing pigs on to weight for meat, then selling pork directly to neighbours or at the farmer's market is also good business. (See *Legislation*). Meat raised to *Organic* or *Freedom Food* standard will sell at a premium. With rare breeds, there is also the *Rare Breed Survival Trust Meat Marketing Scheme*. Finally, there are the local butchers, who will take regular supplies of good pork.

Summary

❏❏☻♥♥££

Space: Requirements depend on how many animals are kept, and whether they are kept out on the field or in a run. On a small scale, a couple of porkers with a house and run will need an area of 30 square metres.

Time: Mixing up your own feed takes time. Proprietary feeds are quicker but more expensive. Cleaning the house daily takes about 30 minutes

Energy: Carrying feed sacks and mucking out regularly is hard work.

Costs: Initial costs include the provision of a suitable house and run with strong walls and a gate, heavy feeding and drinking troughs, and the pigs themselves. Ongoing costs are for feeds and the maintenance of good health.

Useful organisations: *The British Pig Association* Tel: 01923 695295
The Rare Breeds Survival Trust Tel: 024 7669 6551

Recommended books: *Starting with Pigs* by Andy Case

Sheep

The folds shall be full of sheep. (Psalm 65)

Sheep are grazers, so an area of grass is essential. The amount of pasture available and the quality of it, will determine how many sheep can be kept. It is important not to overstock as this can lead to serious health problems. Some pasture may need to be set aside for hay, unless hay is bought in. Farmers keep sheep for lamb meat, and the wool fleece is a bonus. For the smallholder however, the fleece can be a useful end product, particularly if coloured breeds are kept, with wool attractive for spinners. Owners of sheep must be registered. There are other regulations. (See *Legislation*).

Breeds

Britain has over time developed a wide range of sheep breeds to suit local climatic and pasture conditions. The *lowland down* breeds are bigger and heavier than the *hill* sheep, but need a good standard of pasture to thrive. The hill breeds are smaller and hardier, ranging widely over poorer grass conditions. Coloured fleeces have largely been bred out of commercial flocks as the wool industry requires fleeces to be white. There are a number of breeds that are not part of the 'sheep industry' that have attractive coloured fleeces. In addition, sheep are differentiated into *longwools* and *shortwools*. Wool varies in length and fineness in different breeds. Attending agricultural shows during the summer provides a good opportunity to speak to breeders.

Choose a breed that you like, that you will be able to handle and is suitable for your smallholding. It may be possible to keep a ram with your small flock, if there is sufficient space. Most lambs can be raised for slaughter, and others kept to develop the flock. Good meaty lambs can be produced by hiring a ram of a different breed. Many of the coloured and primitive breeds are classified by the *Rare Breeds Survival Trust*, so keeping and developing a flock is a contribution to preserving them for the future. Examples of breeds worth considering are:

Coloured breeds: Soay, Boreray, North Ronaldsay, Shetland, Icelandic, Hebridean, Manx Loghtan, Castlemilk Moorit, Gotland, Black, Badger Faced and Balwen Welsh Mountain sheep, Jacob and Herdwick.

Shortwool and Down breeds: Portland, Dorset Horn, Dorset Down, Wiltshire Horn (no wool), Hampshire Down, Southdown, Suffolk, Shropshire and Ryeland.

A hardy Welsh Mountain sheep of the Torddu (black belly) type.

North Ronaldsay ram.

Longwools: Cotswold, Romney, Leicester Longwool, Lincoln, Teeswater, Wensleydale, and the Blue Faced and Border Leicester breeds.

Hill breeds: Welsh Mountain, Cheviot, Swaledale, and Scottish Blackface.

Other breeds worth considering: Llanwenog, Lleyn and Clun Forest.

Meat Breeds: Texel, Charollais. **Dairy Breeds**: Friesland, Dorset Horn.

Management

Sheep can live outside all year round, but there are two reasons for bringing them inside: first to rest the pasture during the winter when the grass has little nutritional value, and second to provide a good environment for lambing. Bringing in ewes well before the lambing period will produce better lambing results. They can be housed in a polytunnel with boarded and ventilated sides or an airy barn with plenty of straw underfoot. They need a raised feeding trough and hayrack with constant access to fresh water. The housing should be well ventilated but without draughts.

During lambing, electricity is needed for night attendance and the possible use of heat lamps for lambs. When lambing time approaches, the covered area can be converted into pens with the use of hurdles.

Sheep rely on grass for their nutritional needs, so ensure that it is short and free of poisonous plants like ragwort and bracken. Sheep on pasture also need good fencing. Sheep netting is ideal, although expensive for a long boundary. Post and wire fencing together with a good dense hedge may suffice, but be careful if you have primitive breeds as they can climb and jump. Moveable electric fencing can be used to divide the pasture to keep the sheep on fresh ground and minimise the risk of ground based parasites being ingested. Being flock animals, sheep move together which is convenient when they need to be transferred from one place to another.

Sheep farmers invariably use a sheepdog, and the smallholder with a reasonable sized flock can learn to train and use a dog, too. However, with a small flock, sheep can be trained to come when called and to follow when led. The secret is the feed bucket which is an irresistable attraction. Only a few sheep need to be moved and the rest will follow.

Bringing sheep into a confined area for worming and foot inspection will require the use of a number of hurdles. They are an essential part of sheepkeeping. Although sheep gain their food from grass, the quality of it declines in autumn and is of poor quality in winter. At this time they need hay to make up the shortfall, whether they are inside or out. Proprietary pellets can also be fed throughout this period.

Shearing of the wool takes place in summer. A small number can be clipped by hand. A larger flock may need a contractor with power shears.

Keeping rare breeds, such as this Hebridean, helps to conserve them.

Breeding

A flock can be improved and enlarged by careful breeding of replacements. If a ram needs to be hired, this is something to be considered when choosing a breed. If the nearest ram is a long distance away this will be inconvenient for everyone.

Many small flock owners keep their own ram which is ideal. Choose a ram of the best quality that you can afford. He needs to be fertile and not old. Keep a regular check on his health and be ready to separate him from the flock and pen him in the autumn as he is likely to become aggressive at this time. He will need to be well fed and in good health when serving the ewes. The last three months of the year is the period for tupping when the ram rejoins the ewes and serves them.

Ewes selected for breeding should be wormed and turned onto good quality pasture for two to three weeks before tupping. This procedure to bring the ewes to the peak condition is called 'flushing'. They should also be fed supplementary nuts and concentrates during this period. Before being joined by the ram, clip the wool around the tail, removing any soiled material. The ram will need a harness with a raddle crayon when he rejoins the ewes. The colour will transfer to the ewe's wool, showing which ones have been served. Change the colour of the crayon every 17 days. If a ewe shows two colours, the serving did not take first time and the ram may not be fertile. A young ram can serve up to 20 ewes, and an older one up to 40.

A sheep management and lambing course is advisable. (*Merrist Wood Agricultural College*).

Normal tupping time is around 7 weeks, while pregnancy is 5 months, which works well as new lambs have fresh spring grass. Feed pregnant ewes the same diet as during tupping and bring them into shelter as the weather worsens. During the last 2 months of pregnancy, feed concentrates to provide for the growing lambs. Start at 250g (9oz)/ewe/day increasing to 900g (34oz) during the last two weeks, a process known as 'steaming up'.

Vaccinate the ewes against clostridial diseases and pasteurella 4-6 weeks before lambing. This will confer immunity for a while to the new born lambs that take the first milk or colostrum from the mother. The period of lambing needs careful preparation beforehand. Anyone experiencing it for the first time, should either have been on a practical lambing course or have someone experienced to hand. Always keep the vet's number nearby!

The expectant mother needs a draught free place with plenty of fresh straw. As new lambs are born, place them in a box under a heat lamp to keep them warm. When the process is finished, remove the afterbirth, and add fresh straw and provide hay and fresh water. Ensure that new lamb(s) are feeding from the mother, getting that vital colostrum which is only available during the first 24 hours. Orphan lambs will need to be bottle fed with colostrum, then milk substitute thereafter. Dock the lambs' tails with an elastrator after the first day. This will help to protect them against attack from blowflies. Apply lamb identification tags and register them. (See *Legislation*). After the first two weeks while the ewe is fed water, hay and concentrates, the new lambs can be fed water, hay and lamb nuts from a creep feeder. Finally they can all be let out onto new pasture.

Health

Feet need to be checked regularly as foot infections are quite common. Any sheep kneeling or lying to graze should be looked at. Treat any wounds with anti-bacterial spray and isolate the animal until it has recovered. Internal parasites can be prevented with a regular worming programme.

Ewes should be wormed at 3 and 6 months after lambing. Worm lambs at 6 weeks, then every 3 weeks until the threat of worms has subsided. If lambs are on fresh grass it is not necessary to worm them as often.

Flies can be a problem in the summer months. They lay their eggs in wounds or soiled parts of the fleece. These hatch into maggots which feed on the flesh. This serious condition can be prevented with a 'pour on' treatment beforehand. It may need to be applied more than once. Flies can also be discouraged by clipping off badly soiled parts of the fleece.

Sheep need to be vaccinated regularly against clostridial diseases and pasteurella. Ewes should be vaccinated at 4-6 weeks before lambing, and lambs at 10 weeks with a booster injection about 4-6 weeks later. Orf is a viral disease resulting in blisters around the mouth. Use an anti-bacterial spray and wear disposable gloves as the disease can transfer to humans and lead to serious illness. Pregnant women should also avoid helping at lambing time, to ensure that infections are not passed to her and her baby.

Summary
□□□☺☻✋✋££

Space: Several acres of good grass are needed for even a few sheep, to enable the rotation of pasture and to produce hay, unless this is bought in.

Time: Even a small flock is time consuming, with daily feeding and care. Periodic attention to foot trimming, dagging, worming, shearing, tupping and lambing is needed, while summer brings problems like blowfly attacks.

Energy: It can be strenuous. Being able to handle sheep for a range of tasks is essential. If this is likely to be a problem, choose a small docile breed.

Costs: Capital expenses include purchase of stock, equipment: hurdles, drinkers, hayracks, electric fencing to subdivide the pasture, and a field shelter or barn. Ongoing expenses include feeds and medical supplies.

Useful organisations: *National Sheep Association* Tel: 01684 892661 www.nationalsheep.org.uk
British Coloured Sheep Breeders Association Tel: 01884 36202 www.bcsba.org.uk
British Wool Marketing Board Tel: 01274 688666 www.britishwool.org.uk
Rare Breeds Survival Trust Tel: 024 7669 6551. www.rare-breeds.com

Recommended books: *Starting with Sheep*. Mary Castell.
Practical Sheep Keeping. Kim Cardell. *Sheep Ailments*. Eddie Straiton.

Goats

Into the pen, goodnight goats, shut the door and away.
There they are in the morning light, in the big barn full of hay!

(Daisy - aged 10. 2004)

Goats are browsers, preferring a range of branches and herbage to grass, so have to be managed in case they cause damage to young trees and shrubs. It is possible to keep a goat or two without having much land, but organising their feed requirements in this case can be time consuming.

Goats are social animals, so at least two need to be kept. They are intelligent and curious, and respond well to care and attention. Being natural climbers, they like having logs or boulders to jump on. Anyone keeping goats must be registered to do so. (See *Legislation*).

Part of the business of keeping dairy animals is rearing young. A good quality goat mated with a good male will produce good quality kids. Milking animals are time consuming and a tie, as they need to be milked twice a day, seven days a week when they are in production. Joining the local goat club provides a valuable source of support and information.

When buying goats, ask the seller for the milking record of the mother. The body with overall responsibility for goats in the UK is the *British Goat Society*. It defines standards for goats and milk recording at shows and keeps a register of pure breeds. The local goat club will be affiliated to the BGS.

Breeds

Most goats are kept as dairy animals which can provide the household with milk, yoghurt and cheese. There are also breeds kept specifically for their fibre or meat. Choose a breed you like and buy the best quality stock that you can afford. A poor milker costs nearly as much to feed as a good one.

Dairy Breeds

The **Saanen** is a white goat originating from Switzerland; the **British Saanen** is a larger version and the best milker of all the breeds.

The **Toggenburg** and **British Toggenburg** have a similar lineage. They are brown goats with white face stripes and are good milkers.

The **British Alpine** is like a BT but is black instead of brown, but still with the white face stripes. It is a good milker.

The **Anglo Nubian** is a developed version of a North African goat. It has a Roman nose, pendulous ears and a smooth coat. It comes in many colours but is usually brown. It is not a big milker, but the milk is high in butterfat. The **Golden Guernsey** and **British Guernsey** are attractive goats with a golden coat. The BG is larger and has better milking qualities.

Have all the housing and facilities ready before buying livestock and make sure that the animals are healthy, bright and responsive. This is a British Toggenburg goat in its pen in the goat house which is light and airy. Each pen has a hay rack at the back and a waterbucket that can be filled from the central passage.

Other Breeds

Angora goats are white with shorter legs, like sheep. They are kept for their mohair fibre and are not usually dehorned.

Cashmere goats are also kept for their fibre but are few in number.

Boer goats were developed in South Africa as a meat breed. They are hardy, stocky, and docile brown and white goats, but are few in number in the UK.

Pygmy goats are small goats originating in Africa. They are kept as pets, coming in a range of colours and are not usually dehorned.

Bagot goats are an ancient British black and white breed. They are classified as rare and are normally to be found in *Rare Breed Centres*.

Buying

Members of the local goat club will be helpful when it comes to finding your first goats. Buying locally will also provide a chance to visit the breeder, and to look at the herd and milking records. If you cannot find what you need locally, try other nearby goat clubs. I kept goats for many years and had regular contact with three associations in my area. Goatkeepers also advertise in smallholding magazines. If you have decided on a particular breed, contact the national breed society secretary who should be able to give you a list of reputable breeders. For further details on buying, see Page 17.

Management

All milking animals need to be fed sufficiently to enable them to continue to provide milk. A milking goat's daily needs are 450gm (1lb) for bodily maintenance plus 400gm (0.9lb) for every litre of milk produced. Thus a milking goat giving a total of 1.1 litres a day will need a twice daily feed of 450gm (1lb). There should always be fresh hay in the hayrack and constant access to clean water. A milking animal drinks a lot of water, so this needs to be checked regularly, particularly in hot summer weather.

All goats need a balance of roughage - twigs and plants - and concentrates that have a greater nutritional value. Goats confined to a yard need their roughage plants brought in and placed in a large rack. Be careful not to collect poisonous plants. A plant identification book is a good investment. Food that falls from the rack onto the ground will be ignored. This is part of the goat's instinctive behaviour. In winter, fodder and root crops can be given, but should always be balanced against a basic proprietary feed.

In good weather goats can be left in the field. They often prefer hedges and overhanging branches so protect these as necessary. The effect of goats browsing on a field of large leaved weeds improves the pasture over time. Make sure that any poisonous plants such as ragwort are removed. There must be secure fencing as an ambitious goat can jump over a 1.2m (4ft) fence. Electric fencing can be used, and is also useful for subdividing the pasture to keep the goats moving on to fresh ground, thus helping to minimise the build up of parasites. Goats do not like too much heat or rain so need somewhere to shelter if weather conditions change.

Apart from a field shelter, there needs to be a house with goat pens equipped with hay racks and drinkers, where they spend the night, especially in the winter months. The pens need fresh straw as bedding and a mineral lick to avoid the possibility of mineral deficiencies in some soils. There should be a separate milking area that can be washed down each day, as well as a food storage area. Goats can be milked on a low platform with a tether and feed bucket at one end. Concentrates should be stored in strong steel or plastic containers and any spillage immediately cleared away to avoid attracting rodents. Gates on pens and fences need to be very secure as goats are curious and adept at undoing them.

Kids and kidding

A dairy animal won't produce milk without giving birth to young, so kidding and raising kids is part of the goatkeeper's year. Male goats are large, strong and very smelly. They are usually kept by specialised breeders only. When a female comes on heat this will be apparent from a lot of bleating and tail wagging. She is ready to be served so the procedure for doing so must be implemented without delay. There are two ways to do this. Find a suitable male of the required breed in your area and arrange to take your goat there straight away. Alternatively, use artificial insemination. AI straws can be bought beforehand and stored in the freezer, so insemination can take place without the hassle of transporting goats, possibly more than once if mating isn't successful first time. Another advantage of AI is that you can be sure that the sperm comes from a proven good quality male. Your goat club will advise on the details and technique needed.

Pregnant goats need to have their concentrate ration increased gradually as the kids develop inside. Beginning at 450gm (1lb) and culminating at 1-1.3kg (2-3lbs) daily. The pregnancy period is normally 5 months but kidding can begin as early as 140 days. Before kidding begins, ensure that everything that is needed is in place. At kidding time no pregnant woman should attend as she could catch a viral infection causing abortion.

A goat normally has a couple of kids but may have more. Birth nearly always takes place naturally without problems, however if she is straining for a long time without a result or if her kids are not in the right position help may be needed from the vet. Always have the telephone number handy! Once the kids are born, check that they are breathing and normal, then treat the remains of the umbilical cord with a veterinary spray. Place them to

Goats out on pasture. They have a field shelter to run to if it rains, and also a covered hay rack.

suckle with the mother, to receive the vital colostrum which provides antibodies against disease. Remove the afterbirth, provide more clean straw and give the mother warm water and fresh hay. After 24 hours, begin feeding the mother concentrates starting with 450gm (1lb) each day and maximising at 1.8kg (4lbs). Worm the mother goat a few days after kidding. Young kids liable to grow horns should be disbudded by the vet. They will now need to be registered with the *Animal Health Office* and earmarked for identification.

Male kids have little value, but can be raised for meat. They can be separated from the mother after 4 days and bottle fed with milk replacer before being killed at 10 weeks. They do not need to be castrated. Young females can be introduced to a little hay and a cut turf of fresh grass after a few days. They can be progressively weaned from the mother and bottle fed if all the milk output is required. As soon as the weather is favourable, mothers and kids should be put out onto clean fresh pasture.

Health

Goats are generally healthy animals and should experience few problems, as long as they are given the necessary protection. Keep a veterinary spray to hand for treating wounds.

A regular worming regime is essential to provide protection against internal parasites. The mother goat needs dosing a few days after kidding. Kids need worming at 5 months, with a booster dose in the autumn. Use tablets, paste or a liquid drench and learn the technique of administering them from an experienced goatkeeper or by attending a course.

External parasites such as lice will need to be treated with an appropriate insecticide. Check and trim feet. Again, it pays to be shown this by another goatkeeper. When milking, always check at the outset for clots which could be the first indications of mastitis. (See below). As with sheep, goats should be vaccinated yearly against clostridial diseases.

Milking

Goats need milking twice a day. This can be by hand or with a milking machine with the appropriate goat teat cluster. A machine will save both time and effort. The first squeezing of the teats should be into a strip cup to check for clots or blood spots which may be the first signs of mastitis. These should always be discarded as they contain bacteria. When hand milking, always use a stainless steel bucket. Afterwards, the milk should be filtered then cooled in the refrigerator. The milk can be put into cartons and frozen if required. It can also be pasteurised by heating.

If you plan to sell milk or milk products, the premises must be registered and the food safety, dairying and labelling regulations followed.

Summary

□□☺☺♨♨££

Space: Buildings are essential for housing, feed storage and a separate milking area. A small herd needs a well fenced field with a field shelter. An excercise yard with a covered area is also useful, particularly in winter.

Time: Milking twice daily, dealing with the milk and washing down are unavoidable and time-consuming daily tasks. Moving goats, replenishing water and hay, and other daily checks also add up. Periodic tasks include foot trimming, worming, kidding and mucking out the pens.

Energy: Keeping goats requires a lot of physical activity. It needn't be too strenuous but goats can be capricious and require unexpected efforts to catch escapees or get them down from a low roof!

Costs: Start up costs could be considerable if you haven't already got suitable outbuildings. Initial costs may include preparation of land, fencing and gates, construction of internal pens and a milking area. There is also the purchase of stock, feeders and drinkers, as well as dairying equipment. Running costs include feed, hay, bedding and health products. If this sounds daunting, remember that most goatkeepers are not rich people, but are great DIY enthusiasts adapting outbuildings with materials to hand.

Useful organisations: *The British Goat Society* Tel: 01626 833168
Breed Clubs and local Goat Societies - details from the BGS.
Recommended books: *Cheesemaking and Dairying*. Katie Thear.
The New Goat Handbook. Matthew Vriends.

Cattle

Cows are my passion!
(Mrs Skewton in Dombey & Son. Charles Dickens. 1848)

Cows are large animals and need plenty of pasture, so can only be kept by a smallholder with sufficient land. Bearing in mind the need to provide for the odd calf, rotating the fields and making hay, then a house cow would be difficult to keep with less than five acres. Keeping more than one, or raising bullocks for meat cannot be undertaken without having a further few acres.

The benefits of a house cow are considerable. She will provide sufficient fresh milk for the family, with a surplus for making butter, yoghurt and cheeses. The whey left over from cheesemaking is ideal for fattening the pigs. Before buying cattle, read specialised books and if possible, attend courses on cattle and dairying topics. Anyone with a cow must register with the *Animal Health Office*. Each animal must have identification, as well as a passport.

Breeds

There are specialised dairy breeds, meat breeds and the traditional dual purpose breeds. The large commercial breeds are rarely kept by smallholders as they are out of scale with a small scale undertaking.

Jersey: This is the most favoured house cow among smallholders. By modern standards it is relatively small, but with a milk output sufficient for the smallholding. The average yield is around 9 litres (2 gallons) a day, and the milk is famously rich, being high in butterfat. If a Jersey is crossed with a suitable meat breed, a reasonable meaty calf can be raised.

Guernsey: Another suitable dairy breed is the Guernsey, if an original strain can be found, as distinct from the more recently developed version.

Dexter: Many smallholders choose the Dexter, which is a small dual purpose breed. It is suitable as a house cow and also as a small scale meat producer. There is a lethal gene in this breed so it is advisable to avoid breeding the shorter legged versions.

Other dual purpose breeds worth considering are the **Dairy Shorthorn, Shetland, Kerry, Galloway, Gloucester** and **Irish Moiled**.

There are no small beef breeds, but a number of the traditional breeds are suitable for the smallholder with sufficient land. Many breeds have been developed into larger animals, but the original types are often still available. Worth considering are the **Hereford** and **Aberdeen Angus**, both of which

The Jersey is the smallholder's favourite house cow.

mature quickly. The **Beef Shorthorn**, the **Galloway** and the **Welsh Black** are also beef breeds. The **Highland** is a slow grower but may be found in Scotland where it does well in harsh weather conditions. Since the BSE outbreak, cattle have to be slaughtered by 30 months, so the slower growing breeds may need some supplementary feeding to get them up to slaughter weight within the time. See Page 17 for information on buying cows.

Management

A cow needs 0.4 hectare (1 acre) of good pasture, but beef cattle can be raised at 3 animals on 0.8 hectare (2 acres). Fencing needs to be 1.2m (4ft) for dairy cows and 1.5m (4ft 6ins) for beef cattle. It also needs to be strong.

Cows need a field shelter, and if they are brought inside during the winter, they require a waterproof, well ventilated area with plenty of straw. As grazing animals, cattle get their nutrients from grass throughout the spring and summer. Ensure that there are no poisonous plants such as ragwort in the pasture. Use the pasture to the best advantage by rotating the grazing area to avoid the ingestion of parasites. The pasture will also need to be fed and rested during the winter. In autumn, the value of the grass declines and the cattle will need supplementary feeding with hay. Fodder crops such as roots and brassicas can also be added to their winter diet. If hay and fodder crops are grown on site, land will need to be allocated for them.

Fresh water should be available at all times. This is particularly important for milking cows. In hot weather a cow can drink a considerable amount, so a good sized trough in a shady place will need to be regularly topped up with a hose.

Milking cows will need cereal based concentrate rations of an appropriate amount related to their milk output. This can be fed twice a day at milking time. There are organic concentrates for those producing an organic end product. Milking needs to be undertaken twice a day, at around 12 hours apart, in a separate milking parlour that can be easily washed down. A house cow can be milked by hand or with a small milking machine. The procedure is similar to that detailed for goats. Using the milk for dairy products is covered later in this chapter.

Breeding

For smallholders, keeping a bull is not practical or necessary. Artificial Insemination is widely available. Cows coming into season become restless and moo a lot. Heifers are usually served at 15-18 months old, and pregnancy is nine and a half months. With a pregnant cow already milking, production will need to be gradually tapered off. To achieve this, the amount of milk taken is reduced, taking less each time, to dry her off completely two months before birth. In fine weather calving can take place outside in a wind sheltered spot. Inside, the cow will need plenty of fresh straw.

A cow should calve without help, but if she gets into difficulties call the vet immediately. As with sheep, some practical experience of the birth process gleaned from going on a course, will be invaluable.

The new calf will need to suckle as soon as possible to get the vital colostrum milk which is available for the first 24 hours. This contains vital nutrients and antibodies essential for its well being.

If the new calf needs to be disbudded of horns, this will need to be done by a vet a few days after birth. All new calves must be registered and tagged. Bull calves that are to be raised for meat will need to be castrated, using an elastrator. Again, practical tuition on a course is vital.

Separate the calf from the mother after 5 days and bottle feed it with milk substitute twice daily until it is six weeks old. With encouragement it will soon learn to drink from a bucket, rather than suck. Feed water, hay and calf concentrates from one week old. After six weeks, wean the calf off the milk ration and switch to calf weaner pellets with the hay and water. Increase the weaner rations daily from around 90gm (3oz) up to 1.3kg (3lb) by 9 weeks. During mild weather, the calf can be put out to fresh grass for up to 2 hours a day for the first couple of weeks, gradually increasing the time.

An Aberdeen Angus/Jersey cross calf being reared for meat.

Health

The consequences of BSE have resulted in the UK having some of the most stringent regulations in the world. The small scale cow owner has little to fear regarding serious illness, providing that healthy stock is bought in the first place, that basic hygiene is maintained, the animals are fed properly and kept on fresh grass.

A vaccination against clostridial diseases is normally administered in the spring as the cattle go out on grass, with a booster follow up a few weeks later.

Feet: Check feet regularly and trim the hooves when necessary.

Worms: Signs of worms are a dry staring coat and a persistent cough. Obtain an anthelmintic from the vet and follow the instructions as to dosage and administration.

External parasites: Flies, mites, lice and other bugs can be a nuisance during the warm months. There are a number of effective treatments available.

Scouring (diarrhoea): This can arise from several causes. If it is accompanied by a poor coat, suspect worms and treat accordingly. If not, it could be caused by too much lush grass. Bring the cow or calves in and feed on just hay and water for a day. If this does not work, seek advice from the vet.

Mastitis: Always test for mastitis with a strip cup at the outset of milking to see if there are any lumps or clots in the milk. Again, if part of the udder feels unusually hot this could be mastitis. It can be dealt with by an antibiotic injection in the infected quarter. The milk from this quarter should be discarded as required by the treatment. Organic farmers not wanting to use antibiotics can apply homoeopathic treament.

Notifiable diseases: There are diseases which are notifiable by law including foot and mouth. A basic knowledge of these diseases and their causes and symptoms will be very helpful. Keep a specialised book to hand and if concerned contact the vet without delay. See *Legislation* for further details.

Summary
☐☐☐☺☺🐾🐾🐾£££

Space: Even one house cow needs several acres so that hay can be cut and she can be moved onto fresh ground. There also needs to be a field shelter, feed store and milking parlour. Milk storage and dairying activities will need their own areas.

Time: Daily milking, dealing with the milk and washing down are the basic demands, together with supplying hay, concentrates and water. Periodic tasks include hoof trimming, worming, calving and calf rearing, maintenance of fences and regular mucking out.

Energy: Caring for cows is a very physical activity, but apart from heaving feed sacks and hay bales about it need not be too taxing if you are well organised.

Costs: Capital expenditure will be considerable if there are no suitable outbuildings or if fencing needs renewing. There is also the purchase of stock, hurdles, cattle and dairying equipment. Ongoing costs include concentrate feeds, hay if you cannot produce your own, and health products.

Organisations
Jersey Cattle Society. www.jerseycattle.org
Dexter Cattle Society. www.dextercattle.co.uk

Recommended books
Caring for Cows. Valerie Porter.
Cattle Ailments. Eddie Straiton.

Dairy products

Surplus milk can be used to make yoghurt, butter, ice cream and soft and hard cheeses. Those with cow's milk can also produce cream or clotted cream. It is beyond the scope of this book to provide instructions on all these processes but highly recommended is the book *Cheesemaking and Dairying* by Katie Thear. This is a step-by-step, illustrated guide to making all the dairy products, and it is applicable to both home and farm producers.

It is essential to have pristinely clean conditions for dairying, whether they are carried out in the kitchen for home consumption, or for sale. If any dairy products are offered for sale, the producer must be registered and meet all the dairying and food safety regulations. Below is a brief summation of the kind of products that can be made from a milk surplus.

Cheese: Milk is first pasteurised to kill off harmful bacteria, then a purpose-made starter culture to produce the required acidity is added. Rennet is added to coagulate the milk, turning it into curds and whey. The curds are then salted and ripened. If a hard cheese is to made, the curds are pressed.

Equipment will be needed to filter and pasteurise the milk, together with a range of other items for measuring temperature and acidity, for cutting curds and for draining them. To make a hard cheese, a cheese press will also be needed. Finally, ingredients such as rennet and freeze dried starters are essential. Depending on the processes used, there are a range of soft and hard types of cheeses that can be made:

Curd and cream cheeses need no ripening period and are ready straight away.
Soft ripened cheeses need a brief period of ripening before being ready.
Semi-hard cheeses have been lightly pressed, for example Caerphilly.
Hard cheeses such as Cheddar and Cheshire have been pressed hard to remove much of the liquid content before being left to mature.
Inoculated cheeses where moulds are introduced, eg, Danish Blue.

Yoghurt: To make yoghurt, the milk is heated to 82°C then cooled to 43°C, when a yoghurt starter culture is added. It is then placed in a protected environment for 24 hours. A large vacuum flask is ideal.

Butter: To make butter, the cream is skimmed from milk and then put into a butter churn. As it is agitated, it gradually forms particles of butter that coalesce into a mass. This is then rinsed in cold water, drained and salted if required. To make butter regularly, a cream separator would be useful, while a butter churn would be essential.

Other dairy products that can be made are clotted cream, sour cream and ice cream.

Alpacas and Other Livestock

Trying something different, learning new ways - this is the stuff of dreams.

Alpacas are members of the camelid family, which also includes llamas and camels. While the latter have been bred for travelling and as pack animals, alpacas have been kept for their fine wool. They come from South America and although they have been available in the UK for more than ten years there are still relatively few available. The numbers are slowly growing and there is a steady demand for stock. This is reflected in the prices which are high, with buyers taking on a few animals and building up their own herds. In the medium term there is some return from the sale of fleece or wool and young animals, but alpacas are essentially a long term investment for those with enough land and cash to spare.

Alpacas come in a range of 22 colour variations of brown, black, grey and white. The following breeds are available:

Huacaya: This is the most common breed. It is a hardy animal with dense wool extending to the legs. They are available in all the colours and have a wavy wool popular with spinners.

Suri: Normally white or fawn in colour with a long silky fleece. It does well in mild climates like Australia. There are still not many available in the UK.

Chili: These are halfway between Huacayas and Suris. The fleece is less dense and much softer than the huacaya but without the straight staples of the Suri.

Alpacas are browsers seeking a range of plants from the pasture. They also need regular concentrate feeds to supplement their diet. These are available from specialist feed suppliers. They can be stocked at 4-5 per acre (12-15/hectare). A 4ft (1.2m) fence is all that is needed and sheep netting is ideal. They can be sheared in the summer - a job for two people. The fleece should weigh around 3 kilos. When resting the pasture during the winter period, the alpacas will need a well ventilated barn and regular leafy hay to substitute for the grass.

Breeding can begin at 14 months for females and 2-3 years for males. The long gestation period is 335 days, and the young are weaned at 6 months. Young alpacas are known as crias and weigh 6-7 kilos at birth. There is normally just one baby. Breeding takes place all year round and birth is normally during the day. As far as health is concerned, Alpacas are hardy and not susceptible to footrot or flystrike. Kept on soft ground, they need their hooves trimmed every 4 months. Vaccinate the young at 30 - 60 days against clostridial diseases and adults at 6 monthly intervals. Worming them can take place at the same time. Shearing is similar to sheep shearing, except that the animals are standing while this takes place.

Llamas

Llamas are larger than alpacas but are similar in terms of their requirements and management. They are less expensive to buy but there is no annual fleece. They are usually kept as pack animals for llama trekking but are also useful as companions for solitary animals or as guards for lambs or poultry, chasing away predators, such as the fox.

Ratites

Ratites are a family of large birds that include ostriches, emus and rheas. Ostriches are large, around 8ft (2.4m) high and potentially dangerous, needing strong high fencing and housing. They are classified as wild animals and a licence is needed to keep them. A female will produce up to 70 large eggs a season and special incubators are needed. Ostrich meat is low fat and one bird can produce enough for 50 diners. Unfortunately in the past, there were problems with a too rapid expansion of this market, with high prices attracting speculators and dodgy dealers. Owners also ran into problems with slaughtering and marketing, not to mention bad publicity from welfare activists. Things have settled down now, but ostriches are not advisable for the new smallholder.

Emus

Emus are smaller at around 5ft (1.5m) high and more manageable than the ostrich. They are also classified as wild animals and are kept for their meat, leather and oil. They are monogamous, mating for life and are best kept as pairs in large pens with plenty of running space. An unusual feature of emus is their eggshells which are dark green. The eggs therefore have a commercial value in the crafts market .

Rheas

Rheas are about the same size as emus, but they are not classified as wild and therefore do not need a licence. They can be kept at about 20 birds/acre (25/hectare) and need fencing around 5ft 6ins (1.7m). They need to be able to run so need a paddock at least 230ft (70m) long.

All the above livestock need considerable land and investment, and are only recommended for those who are able to do the necessary research and can be assured that they represent a practical proposition.

Smallholding Maintenance

Don't clap too hard, it's a very old building! (The Entertainer. John Osborne)

Buildings

Outbuildings, barns, sheds, and field shelters are extremely useful. They are used for sheltering livestock and poultry and for storing machinery, equipment and supplies. The ideal building will be totally secure in all weather conditions, and strong enough to withstand invasions from predators and robbers. The ideal barn will be constructed of stone or brick with a strong roof and doors, with plenty of ventilation but no draughts.

A building housing poultry needs to be secure against rats and foxes. With timber buildings, check and reinforce the area near to the ground if there is a danger of rats seeking access. Windows and areas open to the weather should have strong, galvanised steel mesh protection.

Livestock are not normally harassed by predators in the UK, but rats and mice will be after their cereal based concentrate feeds so ensure that these are fed well above ground and that there is nothing left after feeding. Feeds should never be left in sacks but always put into metal or strong plastic bins with screw tops or locked lids.

Good ventilation is essential for livestock health, but very low temperatures in winter are not. Wooden buildings in exposed conditions may need to be lined around the walls and provided with a false ceiling. If the main outbuildings are not already wired, it will be advantageous to extend electricity to them to provide winter lighting and power where it is needed. One of the good things about having large empty buildings is that they can be put to a large number of uses and adapted easily with internal partitions. If you have an insufficient number of buildings you can build your own, or buy another building to be erected on site. They can be expensive so secondhand buildings are well worth considering. They can be found among the small ads in farming papers and *Exchange and Mart*. Strong wooden buildings from building sites are often reasonable and the seller will deliver.

The Yard

The ground area in front of and around the main outbuildings should be of concrete or it will soon become a quagmire in winter. It is not difficult to lay concrete once the area has been dug out and prepared. Avoid frosty or very hot weather. A concrete mixer can be hired for the job or a lorry will deliver a load, usually 2-5 cubic metres as required. Ensure that you have sufficient labour to get the job done as wet concrete doesn't wait around. Work quickly, eliminating any air pockets as you go. Remember to 'comb' the concrete so that hooved livestock do not slip on it. If laying a large area, use expansion boards to take account of the expansion and contraction of the concrete.

Boundaries

The boundaries of the smallholding show where your land meets your neighbour's land. Within the smallholding, areas will probably be separated by internal boundaries. These are likely to be walls, hedges or fences. It is worthwhile verifying who is responsible for the outer boundaries and agree this with your neighbours. Where alterations or repairs are necessary, it is better to tackle these at an early stage, as good boundaries make good neighbours and one of the features of country life is how neighbours help each other when needed. It also pays to be forebearing and adaptable. Neighbours aren't perfect and you may be faced with their hedge which has been neglected for years, and which has many gaps through which small animals or poultry can pass. If they are not inclined to do anything about it, you can erect a fence on your side.

Apart from marking out the ownership of land, fences are used largely to regulate animals, keeping some in and others out.There are several types of fences suitable for different applications. The main ones are as follows:

Stone walls: Permanent but skill is needed to build and repair them, as well as a ready supply of stone. They will confine pigs, cattle, geese, chickens and most sheep and ducks, but will not keep out foxes.

Post and rail wooden fence: Permanent and will confine horses, cattle, alpacas and llamas. Young animals may be able to sneak through so netting may be need to be added when required.

Post and Wire fence: Permanent and will confine horses, cattle and may keep in sheep, goats and pigs if there are sufficient wires.

Sheep netting: Moveable and confines horses, cattle, sheep, goats, poultry.

Pig netting: Moveable and will confine everything but it is expensive.

Electric Wire fencing: Effective for confining cattle, sheep, goats and pigs (providing there is a low wire as pigs like to push underneath).

Electric netting: This is useful moveable fencing with different types for varying applications from confining livestock to keeping foxes out.

Any netting is expensive if large distances are involved. The cheapest boundary to erect from scratch is post and wire. It is beyond the scope of this book to describe the whole process, but the key points are to erect and brace strong corner posts, adding an extra post on corners as posts cannot bear wire straining from two directions. Never strain wire from gate posts or trees. Always sink posts well into the ground, especially those taking the strain. What many farms and smallholdings have is a combination of fence types where existing structures are adapted for different applications. A nearby farm has a large field of free range hens. It previously had horses on it and there was an existing post and rail fence. The farmer tacked chicken wire (cheap) to the inside of the fence to keep the chickens in, then added two electric wires. One at 15cm (6 inches) high outside the fence and another along the top to keep the fox out. It worked perfectly.

Finally it is well worth looking after that other permanent boundary the hedge. Many of our hedges are hundreds of years old and were maintained to contain livestock very effectively. Even badly neglected and overgrown hedges can be recovered and it is a skill worth learning. There are short courses available, as well as excellent books and videos.

Pasture

Buying an existing smallholding almost certainly means taking on some pasture fields. It is not uncommon for these to vary and they can be assessed in the same way as the house, outbuildings and fencing. Check whether any of the grass is permanent pastureland. There are few such areas, as most land has been ploughed and seeded. Any pasture is a mixture of grasses, clover, herbs and weeds. If there are too many of the latter than action will be needed.

Waterlogged ground: Fields that are wet and rank with reeds may need to be drained. A drained field needs a ditch. If there is an existing one that is blocked up, digging it out may be all that is needed. If the field still isn't draining, call in a contractor for advice and get a quote for installing a drainage system.

Reseeding: Pasture with too many weeds may need to be cleared and reseeded where there are bad patches, or tackled as a whole. The land can be ploughed or rotovated. Rotovation is best where the soil is thin or peaty, as it is less disturbing to the structure. Check the existing pH value of the soil first. Do all this in the winter, letting frost break down the exposed clods, and then lime. A month later add well chopped manure, slurry or fertiliser letting that work well into the soil before harrowing and drilling with a new seed mixture. There are a number of meadow mixtures available and their suitability will depend on the type of soil, the terrain and how the pasture is to be used. Bear in mind that slurry must not be allowed to drain into watercourses, for this is now against the law.

Repairs: Most pasture is unlikely to need such drastic treatment. Local weed infested areas can be cut right down with hand tools, or with larger areas using a garden tractor or farm tractor with a cutter. Areas with serious woody growth can be attacked with a brushcutter. If you hire one, take care to follow the instructions as they are potentially dangerous. Once the weeds are cut, keep them cut down so that they will weaken and eventually die. If there are oxalis, buttercups and some rushes and mosses, the ground will benefit from being scarified with a harrow. This lets air into the surface of the soil. Again, test these fields to measure the pH level of the underlying soil. Grasses need a pH level of 5.8 to 6.0. Apply lime in the autumn and feed with chopped manure, slurry or fertiliser a month later. If there are bare patches, these can now be reseeded with a meadow mixture by direct drilling. In the spring, apply calcified seaweed to the new growth which maintains the pH value and supplies essential nutrients. Once new grass is growing well, it can be lightly grazed by sheep, calves or goats. Avoid cattle or horses until later when it is fully established.

If there is a plan to raise organic meat from the fields in the future, ensure now that no inorganic fertilisers are used in building up the pasture.

Fodder crops

During the winter months, grazing and browsing livestock are unable to get much nutrition from the fields and need other sources of food to carry them through until the spring. Preserved grass like hay is their daily staple food so ensure that you have sufficient supplies. If you have it, silage (pickled grass) is also good but it is not feasible to make this on a small scale.

Both ruminants and pigs will benefit from eating roots and brassicas. Surplus carrots from the kitchen garden are welcome, as are a range of fodder crops grown specifically for animals. They can be grown in rows on the field and either lifted or strip grazed directly row by row controlling the consumption by means of an electric fence.

Fodder crops consist of roots like fodder beet, mangolds, turnips or swedes and brassicas such as cow cabbage and kale. They can be sown in spring and thinned and weeded with a hoe during the summer. All these crops can be fed to ruminants and pigs. Other crops include comfrey which is best grown in a permanent bed. Young leaves can be fed to poultry and goats will eat leaves fresh or wilted with hay. Field beans can be sown during the winter and after harvesting can be chopped up or ground to provide extra protein in the animals' winter feed. Finally, Jerusalem artichokes can also be planted during the winter and the chopped tubers fed to goats, or left in the ground for pigs to root out and eat.

Legislation

Regulations and codes of practice with regard to livestock are constantly being changed and updated from amendments to UK and European law. At the time of writing, there is also a draft *Animal Welfare Bill* which aims to cover all domestic and captive animals. It is essential to get information fom the following sources before embarking on an enterprise.

Welfare
There are *Codes of Recommendations for the Welfare of Livestock* available for all poultry and livestock. The booklets are free and available from *DEFRA Publications* or the local *Animal Health Office*.

Registration
All livestock (but not poultry) must be registered with the *Animal Health Office (AHO)* department of the local *Trading Standards Office*. Even one cow, one pig or one goat will need to be registered. An exception, for poultry, is if 250 or more breeding birds are kept.

Selling eggs
Surplus eggs can be sold at the gate, to friends and neighbours, and on a market stall, without the need to register, but they must not be sold graded into sizes. If this is to be the case, or if eggs are sold through shops or other retailers, the producer will need to be registered with the *Regional Egg Marketing Inspectorate* of the particular area, as follows:
Midland and Wales: Tel: 01902 693145
North and North-East: Tel: 01132 309669
Eastern: Tel: 01223 462727
Western: Tel: 01179 591000
Southern: Tel: 01189 392215

Standards
Recognised marketing standards for poultry, livestock and animal products are available from the organisations concerned:

Organic standards: These are available from *UKROFS (United Kingdom Register of Organic Farm Standards)* Tel: 0207 238 5915 . www.defra.gov.uk
or from one of the organisations that are licensed to act as certification bodies. These include the following:
The Soil Association. Tel: 0117 914 2412. www.soilassociation.org
Organic Farmers and Growers Ltd. Tel: 01353 722398.
Organic Food Federation. Tel: 01362 637314.
Irish Organic Farmers' & Growers' Association. Tel: 00 351 830 7996.
Scottish Organic Producers' Association. Tel: 01786 841657.
DEFRA also has an Organic Helpline - Tel: 0117 922 7707
Other standards: *Freedom Foods Ltd*, a branch of the RSPCA has produced a set of standards known as *Freedom Food Standards*. Tel: 0870 754001.

Identification

All farm livestock need to have an identification number using a tattoo or eartag. Cattle also need to have a separate passport. Details are available from the *Animal Health Office*.

Movement

Current requirements on the moving of livestock are available from the local *Animal Health Office*. They will provide a movement licence called *Schedule 1 Holding Movement Record*. This is necessary when livestock are moved from one site to another. Copies must be kept.

Transport

The *Animal Health Office* has details of the current regulations for transporting livestock. Relevant regulations are *Welfare of Animals (Transport) Order 1997.*

Slaughter and Meat

Casualties that have to be slaughtered on the farm and removed, must be killed humanely. For help contact the vet, *Animal Health Office* or *The Humane Slaughter Association* Tel: 01582 831919. Casualty animals must be incinerated according to the requirements of current legislation.

Slaughter of animals for meat is not normally permitted on site. Animals must be sent to a licensed abbatoir that is governed by the *Fresh Meat Hygiene and Inspection Regulations.* Meat is butchered, inspected and packed according to these regulations. The meat is then returned bagged and can be sold, provided that the premises are registered with the local *Evironmental Health Department* of the local authority. They need to be satisfied that the *Food Safety Act* and the *Trades Description* and *Labelling* requirements are being followed. Where small numbers of poultry are concerned, the producer can slaughter them on site, as long as the provisions of the *Welfare of Animals (Slaughter or Killing) Regulations* are met. This requires electrical stunning before slaughter.

Medical Records and Practice

You are required to keep a record book of all veterinary products purchased and administered. This is referred to as a *Schedule 2 Veterinary Medicine Administration Record.* Keep all the vet's bills as they will include some of these details. The record book must be scrupulously kept as it is open to inspection by *DEFRA* officers. Unused medicines must be disposed of safely and can normally be returned to the vet. Ensure that the withdrawal periods (the time that must elapse after the end of medication) are adhered to regarding the slaughter of affected animals or the taking of milk or eggs for human consumption.

Notifiable Diseases
Notifiable diseases must be notified to the local *DEFRA* office without delay. They include fowl pest, brucellosis, foot and mouth disease, swine fever and sheep scab. A full list is available from the *Animal Health Division* at *DEFRA*.

Zoonoses
Some diseases, such as salmonella, campylobacter and cryptosporidium, can be transferred from animals to humans (Zoonoses) and can also be serious. A list is available in *The Occupational Zoonoses* available from *DEFRA*.

Selling milk and dairy produce
Milk is recognised in law as coming from cows, goats, sheep and buffaloes. Premises producing milk for sale must be registered as a *production holding*. Those processing milk in any way must be registered as a *dairy establishment*. The *Dairy Products (Hygiene) Regulations* apply, as well as other legislation covering every aspect of milk production, handling and processing. Details are available from *DEFRA*, the *Environmental Health Department* or the *Dairying Inspectorate*.

Selling food products
All food products offered for sale (including dairy products, honey, etc) must conform to the following legislation: *Food Hygiene, Weights and Measures, Labelling and Packaging, Trades Description*. Details are available from the *Environmental Health Department* and local *Trading Standards Office*.

Bee regulations
The *Bee Diseases Control Order* and the *Importation of Bees Order* are in force in relation to the control European Foul Brood, American Foul Brood and Varroa disease. Where honey is sold, the *Honey Regulations* apply, as well as the legislation referred to earlier, under the selling of food products.

Dangerous Wild Animals
Ostriches, emus and wild boar are classified as dangerous wild animals. A permit is required from the *Animal Health Office*, and they are subject to stringent safety regulations regarding fencing and the displaying of warning signs for the public.

Subsidies and Insurance
There are some subsidies available for working smallholders in respect of managing land and keeping certain livestock. Contact your local *DEFRA* office for details. Insurance of the smallholding and its assets is a good idea. This can include liabilities for the livestock. A number of specialised companies are listed on the *Reference* pages.

It is emphasised, again, that the situation with regulations is a fluid one, with changes taking place fairly frequently. It is essential to make your own enquiries and checks.

Reference Section

Organisations

ADAS 08457 766085 www.adas.co.uk
British Alpaca Society Ltd. 01225 340640. www.bas-uk.com
British Beekeepers' Association. 02476 696679. www.bbka.org.uk
British Coloured Sheep Breeders' Association. 01884 36202. www.bcsba.org.uk
British Goat Society. 01626 833168. www.allgoats.com
British Poultry Club of Great Britain. 01205 724081. www.poultryclub.org
British Waterfowl Association. 01892 740212. www.waterfowl.org.uk
British Wool Marketing Board. 01274 688666 www.britishwool.org.uk
Centre for Alternative Technology. 01654 703409. www.cat.org.uk
DEFRA Helpline 08459 335577. *DEFRA Publications* 08459 556000
Farm Animal Welfare Council (FAWC) 020 7904 6531 www.fawc.org.uk
Freedom Food Ltd (RSPCA) 0870 754001 www.freedomfood.co.uk
Humane Slaughter Association 01582 831919 www.hsa.org.uk
National Farmers Union (NFU) 0207 331 7200 www.nfu.org.uk
Organic Farmers and Growers Ltd 01353722398 www.organicfarmers.org
Rare Breeds Survival Trust. 024 7669 6551. www.rare-breeds.com
Rare Poultry Society. 01162 593730
The Soil Association 0117 929 0661 www.soilassociation.org
UKROFS (United Kingdom Register of Organic Farm Standards). 0207 238 5915 www.defra.gov.uk

Publications

The Smallholder's Manual. Katie Thear
The Complete Book of Raising Livestock and Poultry. ed: K. Thear & A. Fraser.
Home Farm. Paul Heiney
Organic Farm Management. Nic Lampkin
Organic Livestock Farming. ed. Younie & Wilkinson
The Organic Garden Book. Geoff Hamilton
The Polytunnel Companion. Jayne Neville
All About Compost. Pauline Pears
The Pruner's Handbook. John Malins
Worms eat my Garbage. Mary Appelhof
Creating a Herb Garden. Jessica Houdret
Starting with Chickens. Katie Thear
Free Range Poultry. Katie Thear
The Chicken Health Handbook. Gail Damerow
British Poultry Standards. ed. Victoria Roberts
Incubation: A Guide to Hatching and Rearing. Katie Thear
Starting with Bantams. David Scrivener
Starting with Ducks. Katie Thear
Starting with Geese. Katie Thear
Keeping Quail, fourth ed. Katie Thear
Starting with Bees. Peter Gordon
Starting with Pigs. Andy Case
Starting with Sheep. Mary Castell
Practical Sheep Keeping. Kim Cardell

Practical Sheep Keeping. Kim Cardell
Sheep Ailments. Eddie Straiton
New Goat Handbook. Matthew Vriends
Goat Husbandry. David Mackenzie
Caring for Cows. Valerie Porter
Cattle Ailments. Eddie Straiton
Cheesemaking and Dairying. Katie Thear
Traditional Woodland Crafts. Raymond Tabor
Basic Blacksmithing. David Harries & Bernhard Heer
Fencing. Elisabeth Agate
Hedging. Elisabeth Agate and Alan Brooks
Woodlands. Alan Brooks
Trees. Planting and Aftercare. Elizabeth Agate

Country Smallholding magazine 01392 888588 www.countrysmallholding.com
Smallholder magazine 01326 213333. www.smallholder.co.uk
Practical Poultry magazine 01959 541444. www.practicalpoultry.com

Services
Cliverton Insurance Brokers 01263 860388
Ecology Building Society 0845 6745566 www.ecology.co.uk
Greenlands Farm Insurance 01970 615561 www.greenlands.co.uk
Newlandowner Management Services 01283 585410 www.newlandowner.co.uk
Ottery Insurance Services 0800 0183495 www.ottery.co.uk

Land and Garden Supplies
Dobies 0870 112 3625 www.dobies.co.uk (Seeds)
Chiltern Seeds 01229 581137
E H Thorne (Beehives) Ltd. 01673 858555. www.thorne.co.uk
Marshalls 01945 466711 (Seeds)
Mr. Fothergills 01638 552512 www.mr.fothergills.co.uk (Seeds)
The Organic Catalogue 0845 130 1304 www.OrganicCatalogue.com (Seeds)
Suttons 0870 220 0606 www.suttons-seeds.co.uk (Seeds)
Thompson & Morgan 01473 688821 www.thompson-morgan.com (Seeds)
Unwins 01945 588522 (Seeds)
Agralan 01285 860015. (Organic controls)
Ashridge Trees 01837 89099 (Hedging and trees)
Buckingham Nurseries 01280 813556 www.bucknur.com (Hedging and trees)
Citadel Products 01789 297456 www.citadelpolytunnels.com (Polytunnels)
Deacons Nursery 01983 522243. (Fruit Trees)
Easybarrow 01354 741133 www.easybarrow.co.uk (Barrows)
Ferryman Polytunnels 01363 83444
Gordon Hill 01404 812229 (Fast-growing poplars and willows)
Knowle Nets 01308 424342 www.knowlenets.co.uk (Crop protection)
The Willow Bank 01594 861782 (Fast-growing willows)
Tracmaster Ltd. 01444 247689. (Two-wheeled tractors)
Amtex 01568 610900 www.amtexlimited.co.uk (Machinery)
Riko Alpine Tractors 01420 479536 www.alpinetractors.com
BSG Tractors and Machinery 01206 212092 www.bsg-supplies.co.uk
Hall Engineering 01404 891105 www.hallengineering.co.uk (Machinery)

Jinma (UK) Ltd. 01952 612424 www.jinma.co.uk (Small tractors)
Siromer Tractors 01253 799029 www.siromer.co.uk
TAFE Tractors 01258 817372 www.tractorsuk.co.uk
Walcot Nursery 01386 553697 (Organic fruit trees)
Wychwood Tunnels 01452 790650. (Polytunnels)

Poultry and Livestock Supplies
Ascott Smallholding Supplies 0845 130 6285 www.ascott.biz
Atlantic Superstore 01986 894745 www.countrysuper-store.co.uk
Smallholder Supplies 01476 870070
Danro Ltd. 01455 847061/2 www.danroltd.co.uk (Labels)
Hi-Peak Feeds 01142 480608 www.hipeak.co.uk
Small Holder Feeds 01362 822900 www.smallholderfeed.co.uk
W and H Marriage & Sons Ltd. 01245 612000 www.marriagefeeds.co.uk (Feeds)
Electranets Ltd. 01452 617841/864230. (Electric netting)
Electric Fencing Direct 01732 833976 www.electricfencing.co.uk
G.A. and M.J. Strange 01225 891236. (Electric netting)
Kiwi Fencing 01728 688005. (Electric fencing and netting)
Hotline Renco Ltd. 01626 331188 www.hotline-fencing.co.uk
Aliwal Incubators 01508 481729
Axt-Electronic 0049 3691 721070 www.axt-electronic.de (Pop-hole closer)
Brinsea Products Ltd. 0845 226 0120 www.brinsea.co.uk (Incubators)
Cyril Bason Ltd. 01588 673204/5 www.cyril-bason.co.uk (Poultry & equipment)
Garden Poultry 01928 787979 www.gardenpoultry.com (Poultry and housing)
The Domestic Fowl Trust 01386 833083 www.domesticfowltrust.co.uk (Poultry, housing and equipment)
Fishers Woodcraft 01302 841122 www.fisherswoodcraft.co.uk (Poultry housing)
Forsham Cottage Arks 0800 163797 www.forshamcottagearks.com (Poultry housing)
Gardencraft 01766 513036 www.gcraft.co.uk (Poultry housing)
Hengrave Feeders Ltd. 01284 704803. (Poultry feeders)
Hodgsons 01833 650274 www.hodgsontimberbuildings.co.uk (Poultry housing)
Interhatch 0700 462 8228. (Incubators)
Jim Vyse 07970 533764. (Poultry housing)
Lifestyles UK Ltd. 01527 880078 www.lifestylesltd.co.uk (Poultry housing)
Lindasgrove Arks 01283 761510. (Poultry housing)
Littleacre Products 01543 481312 www.littleacre.com (Poultry housing)
MS Incubators 01454 329233
Parkland Products 01233 758650 www.parklandproducts.co.uk (Poultry feeders)
The Poultry Pen 01673 818776 www.poultrypen.co.uk (Poultry housing)
Rivers Animal Housing 01233 822555 www.riversanimalhousing co.uk
Barrow Lane Products 01963 34279 www.roosterbooster.co.uk (Winter lighting)
Smiths Sectional Buildings 0115 925 4722 www.smithssectionalbuildings.co.uk
Solway Feeders Ltd. 01557 500253 www.solwayfeeders.com (Poultry equipment)
Southern Aviaries 01825 830930. (Poultry equipment)
SPR Poultry 01243 542815. (Poultry housing and equipment)
The Homoeopathic Pharmacy 01974 241376 (Homoeopathy for livestock)
Galen Homoeopathics 01305 263996 (Homoeopathy for livestock)
M.R. Harness 01299 896827 www.mrharness.co.uk (Livestock halters)
Peter J. Collin 01638 750665 www.frenchall-goats.co.uk (Goat equipment)

Index

Broad Leys Publishing Limited
specialising in poultry and smallholding books

Our other titles include the following:

Starting with Chickens. Katie Thear. £6.95

Starting with Bantams. David Scrivener. £7.95

Starting with Ducks. Katie Thear. £7.95

Starting with Geese. Katie Thear. £7.95

Incubation: A Guide to Hatching & Rearing.
Katie Thear. £6.95

BYO Poultry House (A2 plans and cutting list). £2.00

Starting with Sheep. Mary Castell. £7.95

Starting with Pigs. Andy Case. £7.95

Cheesemaking and Dairying. Katie Thear. £7.95

Starting with Bees. Peter Gordon. £7.95

Keeping Quail. (Fourth Edition) Katie Thear. £7.95
- Published Spring 2005.

We can also supply:

The Smallholder's Manual. Katie Thear. £25.00

Free-Range Poultry. Katie Thear. £19.95

Titles may be ordered from bookshops or purchased direct from us.
Please add £1 p&p per book or 50p for Plans.

Broad Leys Publishing Limited

1 Tenterfields, Newport,
Saffron Walden, Essex CB11 3UW.
Tel/Fax: 01799 541065

(International calls: (+) 1799 541065)
E-mail: kdthear@btinternet.com
www.kdthear.btinternet.co.uk